GHOSTLY TALES
FROM
PEMBROKESHIRE

Brian John

Greencroft Books

2012

A place of rusting gates and fading memories. South Hook Fort, where something very strange happened.........

Chapter One: Introduction

Ghosts, like death, have an undying fascination for the peoples of all cultures, and in the Pembrokeshire folk tradition there are hundreds of stories about encounters with the strange and often frightening inhabitants of the spirit world.

Ghosts come in many forms, and in the folk tradition (and in modern tales of the supernatural) they are sometimes confused with fairies and more often with witches and the Devil.   This is because witches and Pembrokeshire "magicians" were supposed to have the ability to communicate with spirits (both good and evil), and because certain spirits (especially fearsome animals) were supposed to be manifestations or servants of the Devil himself.

But the fairy tradition really has little to do with death or the souls of the dear departed, and fairy stories have a charming and whimsical nature quite unlike most ghost stories.   And ghosts have nothing to do with fairyland. Pembrokeshire fairy stories deserve a volume to themselves. Similarly, it would be improper to devote space in this book to the feats of local witches and wise men.   Most of the stories in which they feature are about curses placed or lifted, about healing, prediction and second sight. The wise men in particular were scientists, herbalists, quack doctors, and amateur detectives as well as conjurors and soothsayers;   and very few of their dealings had anything to do with death, ghosts and the mysteries of the afterlife.

The essential ingredients in ghost stories are death and its consequences in the form of "hauntings" of various types. These hauntings can go on for decades or even centuries, and can sometimes (but not always) be stopped through exorcism.   Most commonly the ghost of a deceased person returns to haunt those who are left behind. Generally it is assumed that the ghost is an unhappy spirit; contented spirits tend to remain in the spirit world, out of sight and out of mind.   Sometimes only one person is chosen for the haunting; he or she may be selected as a "medium" and will see and even talk to a ghost while others are oblivious to its presence.   Many ghosts are attached to a particular place where some tragic event has occurred. Other ghosts have some vital task to perform, such as divulging a treasure location or righting some wrong.

Not all ghosts manifest themselves in visible form, and not all are human. For example, ghostly sounds such as banging, moaning, crying or screaming can occur in a haunted property even where no spectre is ever seen.   Poltergeist activity (in which items fall down from walls, everyday objects are hurled across rooms and smashed, and machines are started or stopped by some invisible force) is a similar manifestation of "spirit energy" often associated with the presence of a teenage boy or girl.   There are stories of ghostly smells; one example is the lavender smell associated with the Lavender Lady of Newport Castle, and another example is the North Pembrokeshire house reputed to contain the ghostly smell of a rotting human corpse which was hidden away under the staircase following a foul murder some decades ago. There are at least two stories of ghostly ships in Pembrokeshire. And the ghostly menagerie of animals is impressive indeed, including horses (which may be headless), little birds, oxen and water monsters, dragons, white dogs from the Otherworld, and the ubiquitous and terrible Black Hounds of Hell.

There are many ghostly stories which relate not to the spirits of the dear departed but to signs, omens and portents of death. In other words, they precede, rather than follow, the moment of death. The most familiar stories are those which concern phantom funerals, corpse candles or falling lights, or baleful voices predicting the death of someone known to the listener. Premonitions, dreams and divinations are similarly eerie, especially for those personally involved.

There is a very old tradition in West Wales about the origins of these supernatural phenomena. According to this tradition, Dewi Sant was a great worrier about the salvation of his flock, for in his view the people thought far too little about their own mortality and about the life to come. He urged them constantly to think about heaven and to prepare themselves for it, but was disappointed when they continued in their worldly ways -- working in the fields, eating and drinking, singing and dancing, and living for the day rather than the morrow. (Perhaps Dewi's expectations were too high, for poor families with mouths to feed could not afford to imitate Dewi's monks by spending much of their time in prayer and contemplation.) For better or for worse, Dewi prayed long and hard for a solution, asking God to give his people signs of the immortality of the soul and of the life to come. He received an assurance that the members of his flock would be given "some presage of death" which would come a few days before death, and which would enable them to make peace with their maker and to prepare for the afterlife.

And so it is that the people of Wales in general, and St David's diocese in particular, were given by God not one but a whole host of special insights or signs to indicate when a death is near. It is said that those who have the eye to see or the ear to hear can still encounter strange phenomena including the corpse candle or "canwyll gorff", the corpse bird or "aderyn y gorff", the phantom funeral or "toili", the death omen or "tolaeth", and the falling light or "tanwedd". And as if these signs and portents were not enough, the Good Lord arranged that under certain circumstances the terrible screaming banshee called "gwrach y rhybyn" would appear, or the dreadful groaning and moaning "cyhyraeth".

Our patron saint may have lived to regret the abundance with which his prayer was answered, for these "death omens" have, over the centuries, signally failed to bring a sense of peace to the sick and dying. On the

4

contrary, they have almost without exception scared the living daylights out of those who have encountered them.

Finally we must consider hauntings of a particularly nasty kind, which involve the unpleasant and often violent creatures which are referred to as goblins or hobgoblins. Those who experience these hauntings find it difficult to describe the creatures which have terrified them. In the Welsh-language tradition there are two ghostly creatures (known by the names "carrog" and "bych") which are so horrid that nobody who has encountered them has ever survived to describe them! Sometimes goblins are referred to as "human or almost human" in form. However, some are apparently part-human or more like goats, and they can subject their victims to unbearable noises and even physical assault. In considering these creatures we have to admit that they may be manifestations of evil, which is why goblins are sometimes associated with the Devil. On the other hand, even the goblin world is inhabited by familiar or kindly spirits who attach themselves to individuals or old houses and who seem to be intent upon performing a variety of routine tasks and good deeds.

We generally accept that ghost stories are morbid and even terrifying. But humour can be found in most things, and there are of course hundreds of jokes in circulation about death, the recently bereaved, and funerals where funny things happen. It is accepted that humour constitutes a release of tension even at the most traumatic of times. So it is that many ghost stories have a spark of humour about them, especially when a "visitation" or haunting is apparently intended to teach somebody a lesson. There is even an old story about an incompetent ghost who needed a little help from a friendly family in order to improve the quality of his hauntings ....

On the following pages there are many Welsh terms which are difficult to translate precisely. The following brief glossary includes the most important of these terms, and provides an insight into the vitality and variety of the local supernatural tradition:

Aderyn y Gorff: a corpse bird, harbinger of death.
Annwn: the underworld or otherworld inhabited by spirits.
Bo-lol: an apparition or bogey-man.
Bwbach: a goblin able to transport people through the air.
Bwca or Pwca: a helpful household goblin or spirit.
Bwgan or Bwcci: unfriendly goblin or poltergeist.
Bych: an evil spirit in the form of a monster.
Canwyll Gorff: corpse candle, a light denoting a death or the passage of a funeral.
Carrog: an evil spirit in the form of a fearsome animal, so terrible that it has never been accurately described.
Ceffyl Dwr: a small beautiful spectral horse or other supernatural animal.

Cipio: transport through the air by a spirit.
Coblin: a goblin, a "knocker spirit" in mines or caves.
Crefishgyn: a spirit.
Cwn Annwn: ghostly hounds, corpse dogs or sky dogs.
Cyhyraeth: death omen, generally heard but not seen; spectre; phantom funeral.
Cythraul: a minor devil.
Diawl: Satan, or the devil himself.
Drychiolaeth: apparition or spectre.
Gwrach y Rhybyn: screaming banshee.
Gwyll: invisible being, ghost.
Gwyllgi: dog of darkness, huge spectral hound, black dog of Baal.
Gwylnos: vigil or wake.
Ladi wen: white lady, ghost dressed in white apparel.
Llamhigyn y Dwr: an unfriendly water sprite.
Offrymu: to exorcise a ghost.
Rhith: an illusion or apparition.
Tan ellyll: will o' the wisp, dancing light over boggy ground.
Tanwedd: death omen in the form of a falling light.
Toili: a phantom funeral.
Tolaeth: death omen such as a tolling bell or the sound of coffin making.
Ychen bannog: oxen of the spirit world, connected with water stories.
Ysbryd drwg: evil spirit or devil.
Ysbrydnos: spirit night, night when ghosts are abroad.

Whatever we make of the matters referred to above, it is interesting to note that the Christian Church has always struggled over its attitude to supernatural phenomena. During the Welsh evangelical revivals of the nineteenth century it became the custom to denounce any acknowledgement of the spirit world as superstition at best and "the work of the Devil" at worst. However, not all ministers of religion have denounced a belief in ghosts, phantom funerals and so forth. For example, the Rev Edmund Jones was a dissenting minister who was well known in various parts of Wales in the early years of the nineteenth century. He travelled widely, and visited Pembrokeshire a number of times. Rev Jones was a firm believer in fairies, ghosts, death omens, and many other things relating to the "spirit world", and he saw no problems in equating these beliefs with his Christian ministry. Indeed, he was scathing in his criticism of those intellectuals and members of the gentry who professed to have a rational explanation for everything, and accused these sceptics of being "estranged from God and spiritual things." Our friend had a number of very strange experiences himself, and as early as 1800 attempted to make a sort of classification of supernatural phenomena. He was universally referred to as "The Prophet Jones" because he had a remarkable ability to predict future events. He wrote two books which together provide fascinating detail on the folk beliefs of Wales in the 1700s. The second of these, a brief tome published in 1813, was notable for its magnificent title, namely: *A Relation of Apparitions of Spirits in the County of Monmouth and the Principality of Wales, with other notable Relations from England, together with Observations about them, and Instructions from them, designed to confute and to prevent the Infidelity of denying the Being and Apparition of Spirits, which tends towards Irreligion and Atheism.*

Tycanol Wood, not far from Newport. Tangled branches, mossy boulders, and black shadows -- just the place for assorted tales of the supernatural.......

During the last century there was a great interest in Spiritualism, and Sir Arthur Conan Doyle and other authors wrote extensively about their experiences in making contact with the inhabitants of the spirit world. There are also many ministers today within the established church and the nonconformist churches who recognise the existence of ghosts and who specialise in exorcisms. Some of them have abilities as mediums themselves, and others work closely with mediums. Rev J Aelwyn Roberts

7

has become well known in Wales for his radio and TV appearances as a "Holy Ghostbuster", and he claims that he has no special powers. Most of his communications with ghosts have been through mediums, although he has experienced all sorts of supernatural phenomena himself. He says that ghosts are sometimes "earthbound" and sometimes troublesome, but that the majority of them are simply preoccupied with unfinished business, sad and lonely and longing for release. As a man with an open mind and a natural sympathy for those who are troubled, he has never been frightened or harmed by a ghost. Some, he thinks, who were bad people in life, can also be bad ghosts in death -- loud-mouthed, bigoted, vindictive or devious. They can single out certain innocent individuals for their hauntings and can leave others quite unaffected. He also believes that there are various ghostly manifestations of evil which can be extremely dangerous even to experienced mediums. And over the years he has developed a delicate understanding of the etiquette which must be employed during ghostly contacts, confirming some of the points made in the stories which follow.

Wherever they come from and whatever they are, the inhabitants of the spirit world appear too frequently and in too many forms to be simply dismissed as "figments of the imagination." The collections of folk tales from Pembrokeshire and other parts of West Wales are full of ghost stories, and every now and then new ghostly encounters and strange experiences are reported in the local press. We dare not dismiss these reports out of hand, however attached we may be to the laws of science and however reluctant we may be to accept "inexplicable" things. Some of us have seen strange things ourselves, or have felt the hairs rising on the backs of our necks in the presence of something unseen. We all know others who have seen ghosts or felt some ghostly presence. So without any attempt on my part to decide what is true or untrue I have tried, in the pages of this book, to report faithfully the most fascinating of the county's ghost stories.

Many (but not all) of the stories on the following pages have already appeared in print in the four volumes of Pembrokeshire folk tales which I published in the 1990s. However, all of these volumes have been out of print for many years. These books were followed by *Pembrokeshire Ghost Stories* published in 1996 and reprinted in 1998; and this book is essentially a revised edition of that last printing, published again now by popular demand.

I hope that through the following pages I will succeed in bringing some of our intriguing ghostly tales to the attention of a new and wider readership. Where possible I have retained the wording of the stories as they were first written down. However, some editing has been necessary, and many excellent tales have had to be omitted.

Brian John   **Halloween 2012**

Chapter Two: Ghostly Tales

The great majority of Pembrokeshire ghost stories relate to the spirits or shades of departed mortals. Sometimes they are recognizable as named individuals, and sometimes they are completely unknown to those who encounter them.

According to the old tradition, ghosts only appear with a specific mission in mind -- for example, to avenge a wrong, to fulfill a neglected duty, or to repay a debt. Once the mission is achieved, the ghostly messenger will disappear, never to be seen again. However, some hauntings appear to have no purpose from the perspective of those who have to suffer from them. Sightings of the Ladi Wen or White Lady may fall into this category; she appears to some people as a lonely, sad spirit, without any malicious intent, condemned by some awful judgment to drift back and forth between the spirit world and that inhabited by mortals. She will visit and revisit the same spot until the end of time, presumably because it was the scene of some unhappy death.

There is a great deal of folklore surrounding ghosts. According to one ancient belief, if one is in a candle-lit room and the candle flame turns blue, this is a sure sign that there is a ghost in the vicinity. If one encounters a ghost with a mission, a certain etiquette has to be followed. There is no need to be frightened, since ghosts are generally quite harmless. It is not thought to be good form simply to run off and get a reverend gentleman who is prepared to conduct an exorcism. It is best to confront the ghost calmly and politely, and to speak to it in the name of Father, Son and Holy Ghost. One must remember that the ghost will not speak until spoken to. But once spoken to, it will reply, and anyone who asks its business is bound into a contract "to see the matter through." (Some unfortunate people who are told the purpose of a haunting and who then refuse to cooperate with the ghost have, in the past, been subjected to all sorts of trouble.) It is not polite to press ghosts too hard on precise dates, or to ask them to describe specific places in detail. One may need to ask a ghost's business three times, but it will then reply in a low, hollow voice. It is extremely dangerous to interrupt a ghost when it is speaking; but once it has finished one may ask further questions, so long as they are strictly relevant to the matter in hand. Once the ghost has given its instructions, they have to be followed to the letter. If they are not, the ghost will first appear "with a discontented visage", and next with an angry one, and finally "with a countenance distorted with the most ferocious rage."

An extreme punishment for those who do not cooperate with ghostly messengers is to be transported through the air "above wind, amid wind, or below wind." Indeed, such a journey may be necessary if business has to be transacted some distance away from the scene of the first ghostly encounter. The unfortunate flying mortal is sometimes given a choice of flying altitude; it is best to choose the middle course, since to fly above wind is to risk being frightened to death by the sight of the ground far below, and to fly below wind is to risk being dragged at high speed through trees, bushes and briars with inevitable consequences in the form of scratches and bruises and even bloodshed.

If one inhabits a haunted house and wishes to be rid of a troublesome ghost, it is not a good idea to attempt an exorcism oneself. This work needs to be done by a medium or a minister of religion, since it is vital to understand the nature of the haunting (for example, the number of ghosts present) and to seek to ascertain the reason for it.

One must assume that ghosts are unhappy and need help if they are to be fully released from earth into the spirit world. They can be banished from properties which they have taken over, but we have it on good authority from the writers of ancient tomes that the thing that ghosts hate most is to be banished to the Red Sea!

On the question of ghostly longevity, "ghostbusters" appear to accept that most (but not all) ghosts fade away after a century or so. They are most easily seen in the generation or two following death, when they may appear indistinguishable from a living person. In some enigmatic stories it is not at all certain whether the central character has died or not.

However, observers have noted that the ghostly manifestations of people who died long ago tend to break up, with the head and the extremities fading first. This may explain why clothing details and facial features are sometimes very indistinct, and why "headless" people and animals sometimes appear in very old ghost stories.

There are hundreds of ghostly stories in the literature, and some of them are so famous that they have been recounted over and again. The most avid collectors of tales of the supernatural were William Howells (1831), Wirt Sykes (1880), Meredith Morris (1899), Sir John Rhys (1901), Ceredig Davies (1911), Marie Trevelyan (1909) and Gwynn Jones (1930). Other tales are to be found in the writings of Giraldus Cambrensis (as long ago as 1188), Richard Fenton (1811), Edward Laws (1888), Mary Curtis (1880), Peter Underwood (1978) and David Parry-jones (1988), as well as in local guide books, newspapers and magazines.

Many old ghost stories have been passed down from generation to generation. Spooky tales keep on appearing, and in 1998 the "Western Telegraph" newspaper carried a report of ghostly encounters at Scolton Manor, near Haverfordwest. Mediums and ministers of religion are still hard at work on exorcisms, and there is no reason at all to believe that ghosts and unseen spirits are fading away or becoming extinct ………

White Ladies

There are many "White Lady" traditions in Pembrokeshire, mostly associated with ancient buildings and with female hauntings by some sad and lonely figure unable to find peace. In the Welsh-speaking areas the term "Ladi Wen" is used. For example, there are reputed to be spectral ladies dressed in white in residence at Manorbier Castle, Lamphey Court, Newport Castle, Carew Castle, St Dogmael's Abbey, Rhos-y-Gilwen Mansion, and Roch Castle. In the 1700's a white lady called "Mallt (Matilda) of the Mist" haunted the valley near Moylgrove, and it was believed that anybody who saw her washing her hands in the stream would die shortly afterwards. She was reputed to appear occasionally at the entrance to Penrallt Ceibwr Farm. The spirits of other ghostly ladies are associated with lonely sites where they met their deaths, either through murder or suicide. Here are a few Pembrokeshire examples.

The Ghyll, Prendergast, Haverfordwest

This is a typical sad ghostly tale dating back to the days of the Civil War in the seventeenth century. In those old times Prendergast, on the outskirts of Haverfordwest, was a distinct village with its own strong sense of community. Near the river there was a fine mansion called Prendergast Place, inhabited by the Stepney family. Like many of the Pembrokeshire gentry, the Stepney family sided with the King during the Civil War. The course of the war in Pembrokeshire was very complicated, and allegiances changed as the Parliamentary tide ebbed and flowed. But the Stepneys remained resolute in their support of the king, and one day a son of the family set off to fight for the Royalist cause, leaving his young wife and children behind.

Accompanied by a small troop of soldiers, he made good progress across Pembrokeshire, sometimes travelling through hostile territory controlled by the enemy. But at last, far from home, he was ambushed by a band of Roundheads. A fierce fight ensued, and among the casualties was young Stepney, dead on the ground in a pool of blood. His body was never returned, and although a message eventually reached Prendergast Place to the effect that the young man had fallen in battle, his wife refused to accept that she would never see him again. She waited, day after day, for his return; and she maintained her faithful and futile vigil until she died a sad and lonely death.

Now her ghost haunts the place where Prendergast Place once stood, and she has been seen many times in the grassy lane which is called the "Ghyll" or "Ghyle" by local people. She is called "The White Lady of the Ghyll" by the older people of Prendergast, having been seen on moonlit nights gliding through the green sward at the side of the road. She has about her an air of utter desolation, and sometimes she is heard moaning softly. Sometimes she is accompanied by a small child. She does not stay to haunt people for long, but after a few minutes subsides into the grey mists which swirl about the damp meadows of the Western Cleddau valley ....

St Dogmael's Abbey

Following the decline and fall of St Dogmael's Abbey, a famous inscribed stone called the Sagranus Stone was used as a bridge over a brook in the old abbey grounds. It was laid face down, so the inscriptions were not badly damaged while generations of local people tramped over it. While it was very handy during the day, it had a fearsome reputation at night.

Many people saw a mysterious ghostly figure (referred to simply as "the white lady") gliding over it at the witching hour of midnight. Consequently, no local person could be induced to walk over the stone when it was dark. Eventually, the stone's supernatural reputation prevented it from being smashed up and used as building material in the 1700s, at a time when the locals looked on the abbey ruins as a very convenient stone quarry.

When the Sagranus Stone was re-erected it became famous throughout the Celtic world, for its Latin and Ogam inscriptions provided the clues for the deciphering of the Ogam alphabet in 1848. Maybe the White Lady of St Dogmael's knew the destiny of the stone, and took on herself the task, over a period of 300 years or so, of protecting it from the desecrations of the abbey by local people.

Newport Castle, one of whose resident ghosts is known as the White Lady or Lavender Lady

Cilwendeg, near Boncath

There is a white lady in occupation at Cilwendeg, near Boncath. She was seen many times prior to its refurbishment as an Old People's Home in 1988. Mr Picton Evans saw her several times and describe her as quite friendly and pretty, and wearing a white dress. He clearly quite enjoyed her company. Other residents and staff experienced small inexplicable incidents, including a mysterious touch on the shoulder, a subdued cough from an empty room, and a sense of someone present but unseen. According to a local tradition the ghost is that of a young lady who was due to marry but who was tragically killed in a horse-riding accident just a few days before her wedding.

Rhos-y-Gilwen, near Cilgerran

Rhos-y-Gilwen is one of a multitude of fine mansions once occupied by the gentry of the Teifi Valley. These houses were once the centres of social life in the valley; but they were also the place where commerce was conducted, and their estates saw many changes in agriculture and land management as the eighteenth and nineteenth centuries progressed. However, the good times could not last, and as the estates declined the sounds of music and laughter faded away. During the last century or so many of the fine houses (including Rhos-y-Gilwen) fell into a sad state of disrepair.

One day in 1990 the old mansion was gutted by fire, and it appeared that it would have to be abandoned. However, the shell of the building was bought by a small group of people who determined to bring it back to life. After years of hard work they replaced the roof, and gradually the restoration of the interior was taken in hand. During the early days of the work the residents were strangely moved on a number of occasions to play the Monteverdi "Vespers", and they began to believe that there was some sort of saintly presence in the building. In particular, they felt this presence on the main staircase and landing. David, one of the residents, had a number of experiences in which he saw the dim shape of a woman standing and watching him. On another occasion a woman resident was standing downstairs waiting for one of her children to come out of the downstairs toilet. She happened to glance into a large mirror in the passage and saw the reflected image of a woman standing behind her. She turned round, but there was nobody there.

There have been other sightings of the ghostly lady; but the consensus is that she is a serene and friendly guardian of the house. Some years ago David inquired in the village of Cilgerran as to the likely name of the saintly lady, and he was told by a very old resident of the village that her name was Mary. Apparently she had been a servant in the mansion many, many years ago. Furthermore, she had been a very religious person; and

13

perhaps this goes some way to explaining the impulse which the residents of the house had in the early days after the fire to sing and play sacred music. The music of Monteverdi must have been familiar to the servants of the house in the eighteenth century. In recent years the white lady has not been sighted, but the new owners of the mansion have noticed that in one of the unoccupied bedrooms a made-up bed is sometimes left with a depression in the bedclothes, suggesting that the white lady has sat there during the night.

Newport Castle's Lavender Lady

Another white lady apparition appears from time to time in the little town of Newport (Trefdraeth) on the north Pembrokeshire coast. Here there is a fine castle which was built by the Normans around the year 1195. In the 1700's the castle was in ruins, but in 1859 the gatehouse was converted into a residence, and what was left of the old stone structure was partly restored. The gatehouse is still used as a private residence, and is still owned by the Lord Marcher of Cemaes.

We should expect a castle of this antiquity to have at least one resident ghost -- and in this case she has often been seen on the banks outside the castle walls. She is said to walk up and down the grassy slope leading to the upper end of Castle Street; and this is precisely where the old castle driveway was located before the present drive was built in Victorian times. If one looks carefully one can just make out the depression in the lawn where the old track once ran. Presumably the white lady is the ghost of some sad soul who lived in the castle in the centuries before it fell into ruin, since she seems determined on her perambulations not to use the "modern" entrance to the castle to the west of the Hunter's Tower. This resident ghost is referred to locally as "the Lavender Lady".

When Mr and Mrs Dean Shields were tenants of the castle they would often smell lavender very strongly, even though there was no lavender in bloom and no lavender scent in the building. On one occasion Mr Robert Humfrey was sleeping in the castle, but woke up to find an old lady standing at the foot of his bed. He was not at all frightened, and felt that she was actually a kind and gentle person.

She may also appear in a very old cottage near the castle. Quite recently a young man named John, who shared this cottage with his girl-friend, was visited by his brother and his family. The visitors knocked on the door, and when it was opened by John the visitors saw three people and not two in the passageway. John turned and he also saw "an apparition" standing behind his girl-friend. The three people who saw it described it as "a misty or shady presence." John had previously assumed that there was some spiritual inhabitant of the cottage, since occasionally lights would be turned on and off in approved ghostly fashion.

The Bishop's Palace, Lamphey

This story is a reminder that if you meet a ghostly white lady you should treat her with sympathy and respect. In 1865 Jonathan Davies was a gardener at Lamphey Court. One night as he was walking from the big house towards the village he saw a ghostly female figure in front of him. This was somewhere near the old medieval palace used centuries before by the bishops of St David's. The lady was dressed in long white robes, and she had an ethereal glow about her. Being a polite fellow, Jonathan said "Good evening", and was disappointed to receive no reply. She walked in front of him for some way and then suddenly disappeared. Later on, as he walked back to the big house the white lady appeared again at the same place. Again she walked in front of him, as if teasing him. By now Jonathan had had a few pints at the local inn and he felt brave, so he decided to give her a swipe with his walking stick. The stick went right through her and he almost fell flat on his face; but then the white lady became angry, and she danced about him wildly for several minutes, making what Jonathan later referred to as "Satanic grimaces" which made his hair stand on end. Then there was a flash of light and the white lady disappeared. Jonathan never saw her again.

The ruins of Lamphey Bishop's Palace.   Near here, Jonathan Davies saw the White Lady.

15

The Road to New Hedges

In the old days there was supposed to be a white lady who haunted a particular spot between Tenby and New Hedges. Before the building of the new A478 road into Tenby there was an old road that ran further to the east, from New Hedges into the town. From this road a lane ran down towards the town reservoirs. There was once a gate here which was called "the spirit gate" by the children who played nearby. Once upon a time a young girl from the neighbourhood used to meet her lover at the gate, but then he betrayed her. So heartbroken was she that she jumped into one of the ponds and drowned. Her sad spirit continued to "keep tryst" at the gate for many years afterwards, frightening the wits out of the local children.

Princess Nest at Carew Castle

In 1975 a family of visitors was enjoying a pleasant picnic lunch in the car park across the millpond from Carew Castle. Suddenly the mother had her attention drawn to a white female figure moving among the castle ruins. The other members of the family saw her too, now appearing at a window, then passing along the castle ramparts, and again disappearing behind a wall. She had a spectral quality about her, and after watching for a few minutes two of the family members crossed over to the castle to investigate. They hunted among the ruins, but neither saw nor heard anything. Other people have also seen the white lady at the castle in broad daylight, and one interesting sighting involved a white-robed figure which appeared in some of the highest windows, where there is no floor to support the weight of a human being. It is widely thought that the White Lady of Carew is the ghost of Princess Nest, a famous and beautiful daughter of one of the most powerful princes of South Wales. She enjoyed a complicated sequence of adventures both in and out of bed, and earned the nickname of "Helen of Wales." Following her marriage to Gerald of Windsor she lived at Carew Castle, but according to legend the real love of her life was the hot-blooded Prince Owain ap Cadwgan who stole her from under her husband's nose in the year 1107. Perhaps her ghost still wanders the castle ruins awaiting the return of her beloved Prince, who met a grisly death when he was ambushed by the jealous husband eight years after the abduction took place.

White Lady at Manorbier Castle

Manorbier Castle was the childhood home of Giraldus Cambrensis, and it has seen life and death over a period of 800 years. One of the three ghosts said to inhabit the castle is a lady in white, who figured in a strange episode during the First World War. At the time a group of soldiers were on duty in the castle, having been detailed to keep a constant watch on the coast for fear of enemy action. At night the soldiers went on guard two by two. One night one of the two guards fell ill, so the sergeant took him off to the doctor and promised his colleague that he would send a replacement as soon as possible. At last the replacement soldier arrived, but he could find no trace of the lone watchman. He searched everywhere, first inside the castle and then in the village outside. At long last he found him lying unconscious on the village green, with his rifle abandoned on the other side of the stream. Clearly the poor fellow had jumped across the stream in a state of panic before passing out.

When the soldier came round he related that he had seen a lady in white coming towards him. He had challenged her, but still she came on, so at last he had fired at her. The bullet had passed clean through her, upon which she disappeared from sight. Alone among the dark shadows of the castle, the poor man had been so terrified that he had fled towards the village as fast as his legs could carry him.

The Haunting of HMS Asp at Pembroke Dockyard

One of the most complicated (and best authenticated) tales of a "white lady" haunting comes from Pembroke Dock, and it is unusual because it concerns not an ancient house but a seaworthy working ship. HMS 'Asp' was a small paddle steamer purchased by the Navy and based at Pembroke Dockyard for surveying work. In 1850 a Captain Alldridge took command of the vessel, and as he was being shown round it by the Dockyard Superintendent he was informed that the ship was haunted. The Superintendent said that he doubted if he could get any of the Dockyard men to work in her, such was her reputation. The Captain greeted this news with a sceptical smile, but the vessel needed to be repaired and refitted, and the work was put in hand. The shipwrights worked on board for a week; but then they came as a body to the Captain and implored him to give up the ship as she would bring nothing but bad luck. The Captain would not hear of it and insisted that the work should continue.

Eventually the refit was completed according to plan. But once the ship began its surveying work under the new captain strange things began to happen. Often the Captain and the other officers heard banging, clattering and strange inexplicable noises in the empty after cabin, which could only be reached by the companion ladder that served his cabin also. He could see from his own cabin anyone who climbed up or down the ladder on their way to or from the aft cabin. The noises continued, and were most prominent on quiet evenings when he sat alone in his cabin reading by lamplight.

On one occasion when the ship was visiting Queensferry in Ireland Captain Alldridge returned on board one night to hear noises coming from his own cabin. He thought he had caught the ghost at last, and burst open the door, only to find that all was just as normal inside, with no ghost to be seen. Shortly afterwards, the Quartermaster burst in with news of trouble on board. The night lookout had seen the figure of a woman standing on the paddle-box and pointing heavenwards. The poor man had been so terrified that he fled from his post, and on being ordered back he went into convulsions. The result was that the Captain, who was made of sterner stuff, angrily had to complete the watch himself.

Later, when the ship was back in the waterway, it was lying peacefully at anchor at Lawrenny one Sunday afternoon. The steward came to the Captain in a state of extreme agitation, having been spoken to by a mysterious disembodied voice. He was so terrified that the Captain had to allow him to go ashore to recover. Subsequently a number of the sailors on board had experiences which terrified them and which caused them to request discharge. On being refused, the men deserted ship, and the ship's surveying work was greatly disrupted as a result.

Captain Alldridge was not a man to retreat from the presence of a ghost on his ship but he had many experiences himself which made his hair stand on end. Once he was woken up in a cold sweat at dead of night by a hand being placed on his forehead. And on many occasions he was woken by drawers in his cabin being opened and closed, and by the banging of his wash-stand top.

Things came to a head in 1857 when the vessel put into the Dockyard again for repairs. On the first night in harbour the dockyard sentry reported that he had seen the figure of a woman climbing up onto the paddle-box, where she stood and pointed towards the sky. Then she came ashore towards him. When challenged, she walked straight through his musket, upon which he dropped it and fled in disarray to the guard-house.

A second sentry witnessed the whole episode and himself fired at the apparition, with no effect. And a third sentry saw the figure enter the old Pater Churchyard, where it mounted a grave and disappeared from sight. All the guards in the Dockyard were so scared by the news of this event that the guard had to be doubled.

However, the departure of the ghost from the ship to the Churchyard signalled the end of the haunting, and the unhappy woman was never seen again. In seeking an explanation for the strange events on board his ship, Captain Alldridge later discovered that prior to being commissioned by the Navy, HMS 'Asp' had been an Irish packet boat.

After one trip, a stewardess had discovered the body of a beautiful girl in the aft cabin, where she had travelled as a passenger. Her throat had been cut, and nothing was ever discovered about her or about the perpetrator of the crime.

A Lady in Black in Newport

Not all female ghosts are associated with an aura of whiteness. This is a story of a frightening female ghost dressed in black. Old Mrs Griffiths used to have a bakery and general store at Gwalia, in East Street, Newport. Sadly, her husband committed suicide, and she never got over the shock. She gave up the shop and moved to a house in Upper St Mary Street in the town, and there she lived for many years until she died. She was a very severe and devout woman -- a pillar of the local chapel community, a stickler for convention, and a strict upholder of propriety. She would be seen every Sunday on her way to Chapel, dressed in black, with her bible under her arm.

When she died her house came into the ownership of a relative who decided to let it out to tenants. And so a young couple moved in. The man was from the locality, but the young lady was from Essex. They dressed rather strangely and had peculiar hair-styles, and in those far-off and unenlightened days they were referred to by the locals as "hippies."

Gradually it emerged that they were not actually married, and that this was a situation that did not worry them in the slightest. But one day the young lady came to see a well-known councillor who also ran a long-established ironmongery in the town. "We're very worried," she said. "We love the house, but we think it is haunted. Every now and then we see this old lady in the house. She stands on the landing outside our bedroom door. She is of medium height, has a rather severe expression on her face, and she is dressed all in black. She seems to be holding a book under her arm. Normally she just stands there for a bit and then she disappears. It's as if she's giving us a ghostly rebuke."

The councillor felt the hairs stand up on the back of his neck, as he immediately recognized the description as that of the recently-deceased Mrs Griffiths. All he could assume was that the old lady, who was not a happy person at the best of times, was offended and angry in her spirit world at the sight of two happy young people living and loving together out of wedlock. The councillor agreed to help, and eventually the Rector of the parish came and conducted an exorcism which removed the ghostly old lady from the house. Now the house is as friendly as any other in Newport.

Ghostly Monks and Nuns

Priory Ruins, Haverfordwest

Many of the writers on ghostly matters have remarked on the frequent occurrence of ghosts in old churches, abbeys and priories. Pembrokeshire has its fair share of ghostly monks, nuns and clerics. One of the most famous stories comes from Haverfordwest. The Augustinian Priory near the river was founded around the year 1200, and it flourished as the most important monastery in Pembrokeshire until it was closed down by Thomas Cromwell in the reign of King Henry VIII.

Although recent archaeological investigations have removed something of the nocturnal "aura" of the place it is still dreaded by local people. The reputation of Priory Ruins as a spooky place goes back several centuries, and to this day there are occasional reports of sightings of a mysterious shadowy figure referred to as the "Spectral Monk".

Very early one morning, around the year 1950, two local women named Martha and Edith were making their way down Union Hill towards their place of work in the lower part of the town. They were well dressed for the weather, with thick winter coats, scarves and mittens. As they walked, frost crystals sparkled on the grass at the roadside, and the branches over their heads were weighed down with white rime ice. Their footsteps echoed about them in the narrow lane, and their warm breath condensed into clouds of steam around their heads. They could just make out the lights of the town ahead of them, making an orange glow in the sky. As they approached the entrance to Priory Ruins they quickened their steps, as they always did, for they did not like the feel of this place. Through the hedge they caught occasional glimpses in the half-light of the sombre crumbling walls of the old Priory, thickly clad in ivy. They walked in silence, and although they could just see where they were going Martha regretted that she had forgotten her torch when she set out for work.

Suddenly Edith grabbed Martha's hand and stopped dead in her tracks. "Look!" she whispered, with a touch of panic in her voice. "What's that in the road by the gate?" And as they stared ahead they could make out a strange glowing light. They watched for a moment, and the glow seemed to materialise into the figure of a monk dressed in a long habit and cowl. With mounting horror they saw that he was moving slowly towards them, with a clawed finger beckoning. Then the black hood fell back, revealing a man's face with dark eyes. The spectral monk came even closer, still making the beckoning motion. The women could bear it no longer. Poor Edith fainted on the spot with terror, and Martha screamed at the top of her voice and fled off up the hill towards home.

Later, regaining her composure, Martha returned to collect her friend, finding that she had recovered consciousness and that the ghostly figure had disappeared. Badly shaken, the two of them returned home in the early light of dawn. They remained in a state of shock for some hours, and refused to go to work that day.

When they related their story to their family and friends, nobody would believe them; but after that they both refused to go to work past Priory Ruins, preferring the longer walk across St Thomas Green and down High Street instead.

The High Street Crypt

There is reputed to be another ecclesiastical ghost in the centre of the town. At the top of High Street there is an old crypt which is thought to have been associated with a monastic house of some sort. There used to be a number of buildings on the corner of Market Street and High Street. One of them was occupied by a chandler in the last century, who used to store his candles in the crypt. Around 1860 there was a watch- maker's shop here, occupied by a Mr Watson. The shop window was closed each evening by a boy employed by Mr Watson. He had to put up the heavy shutters over the glass and lock up before going home. The twilight was almost gone, and dark shadows were creeping across the street. The boy put up one shutter and went into the dark shop to fetch the second, when he suddenly saw the figure of a robed monk in front of him. So frightened was he that he dropped the shutter with a crash and fled home, leaving the shutters and the shop to look after themselves.

About ten years later, when some building operations were going on at the back of Commerce House in High Street, a well was found with a very old skeleton at the bottom of it. In the 1920's a schoolboy from the nearby grammar school saw a monk in a dark habit standing on a wall near the crypt, surrounded by a blue light. There was another sighting of a monk by a workman. When Frederick Warren investigated these ghostly episodes in the 1920's he was told by a local Confectioner of a local tradition that a monk had once been executed in the yard at the rear of his shop.

Ghostly Nun in Monkton Old Hall

When the Rev Tudor Evans lived with his family in Monkton Old Hall, not far from Pembroke Castle, he told a newspaper reporter about a series of very strange events. On many occasions the Vicar was disturbed by heavy knocking on his bedroom door at precisely 4 am. He would get out of bed to see who was there, but as soon as his foot touched the floor the knocking would cease. And when he opened the door there was never anything to be seen. There was also a room in the house which the family dog steadfastly refused to enter, although it happily wandered about in every other room. Even when urged to enter the room the animal refused to budge. One day the Vicar's daughter saw a glow of light coming from the room when she was on the landing outside, and when she opened the door she saw quite distinctly the outline of the head and shoulders of a cowled figure, apparently leaning out of the window and waving its hand.

After this the room came to be known as the "haunted room", and on one occasion a friend of the family slept there. Afterwards he related how he had heard the rustling of long garments around the bed all through the night. On several occasions he tried to light the candle at the bedside in order to investigate the source of the sound, but each time the candle was immediately and mysteriously snuffed out.

The mystery of the haunting at Monkton was solved later when, during repair work in the Church of St Nicholas, Monkton, the remains of a kneeling woman were found bricked up inside a wall in the priest's room. It was later explained that there was an ancient Benedictine priory attached to the church, and the Rev Evans ,speculated that the body was that of a nun who had committed some sin which required penance. He believed that the haunting of the Old Hall was the result of this sin which had kept the nun's spirit "earthbound".

The Black Monk of Caldey Island

In the 1920's there was great interest in the supernatural on Caldey Island, and there were various reports about this time of strange sounds at dead of night, and of sightings of a black-habited monk in the lane near the old priory. Many local people are reputed to have seen him. They believed, in the old days, that he was the ghost of a monk who went mad. Aelred Carlyle, who had bought the island in 1906 for the use of his Anglican Benedictine community of monks, claimed to have seen the shadowy figure on many occasions. Other inhabitants of the island also reported seeing the apparition, which would

appear out of nowhere and disappear quite suddenly.

Perhaps the best authenticated encounter with the phantom monk involved a hard-bitten workman called Arthur Gay. Years later, he told Roscoe Howells that one evening he was going round the greenhouse boilers when he clearly saw a monk in a black habit walking towards him. As he always did when greeting one of the brothers, he pulled his forelock and said "Good night brother." The shadowy monk did not even acknowledge him, but walked straight through the high garden wall and disappeared. Gay was intrigued to discover later on that there had once been a doorway in precisely that position and that it had subsequently been bricked up.

The Haunting of St Buttock's Chapel

Not far from the Murco Refinery (originally built and operated by Amoco) there is a fine mansion which has a long and fascinating history. It was built on the site of St Buttock's Chapel, named after a Celtic saint named Buttock or Buddock. The chapel was used for worship by the monks of Pill Priory, which was less than a mile away.

The old chapel was in ruins by the late Middle Ages, and the first mansion was built on the site during the 1500's. It was rebuilt in 1807 as a stately and elegant home; and since the original name was not suitable for use in refined circles, the mansion was renamed St Botolph's. When Amoco was involved in the construction of the nearby refinery the company bought the house for use as an office and residence for key workers.

One night a worker was woken up by a strange sound which at first he could not identify. Then, when he was fully awake, he realized that the sound was that of a group of monks chanting and praying. Eventually the sound disappeared and the man went back to sleep. Nobody believed him when he related this to his colleagues in the morning; and indeed neither he nor anybody else at the time was aware that the site was once used as a place of worship by the monks of Pill Priory.

So far as we know, this is the only recorded instance of a ghostly haunting by monks in the mansion. However, there is another resident ghost which began to appear after the mansion was bought and converted into luxury flats by Mr and Mrs Beer. The ghost is female, and appears occasionally on the main staircase, dressed in white. She is perfectly harmless and friendly, and some of her visitations are remembered by Mrs Merryl Lloyd, who was brought up in the mansion

Enigmatic Eerie Tales

Stories of white ladies and ghostly monks and nuns are easy to classify, and the stories themselves tend to be relatively simple. But there are a number of tales from Pembrokeshire that are very strange indeed, dealing with people who may or may not have been ghosts or apparitions.

Man or Ghost at Stackpole?

In the twelfth century Elidore de Stackpole was one of the knights who was newly established in the colony of Little England Beyond Wales. The affairs of his estate were in the capable hands of a steward, but one day a young red-headed man who called himself Simon appeared on the scene and took over the steward's job with such panache that nobody thought of rebuking him. First he took over the keys to all the rooms in the lord's house, and then he began to manage all the business matters of the house and land with such prudence and providence that everybody was delighted. Whenever his master or mistress secretly thought of some new item of clothing, or some new food, or some item for the house, it would be miraculously procured by the young man, who would simply say "You wished that to be done, and it shall be done for you."

The lord and lady of the manor appeared to have no secrets from Simon, for he knew where all their most treasured possessions were hidden as well as being able to read their thoughts. They tried to economize and to put some of their money aside as insurance against a rainy day, but the young man took to telling them off, saying "Why are you afraid to spend your gold and silver, since your lives are so short and since your savings will never be of any use to you?" Then he began to display distinctly socialist tendencies, serving the choicest meat and drink to the rustics and hired servants and justifying his generosity by saying that those who laboured hardest on the estate should be rewarded with the most abundant supplies.

At last young Simon let his ambition get the better of him, and he took to making decisions about the running of the estate without any reference to his master or mistress. In effect, he took over the whole estate, much to the irritation of everybody except the well-fed rustics. Then it was noticed that he never showed any signs of devotion to God, and he never went to church. Furthermore, nobody knew what happened to him at night, for he never slept in the manor. And yet he was always in his office bright and early every morning, going about his duties.

At last some of the family took to spying on him, and it was discovered that he spent the nights near a mill where there was a pool of water. Furthermore, he could be seen there talking to shadowy unknown persons. This convinced Elidore that something fishy was going on, and he summoned Simon to his room to give him his discharge and to ask for the keys of the estate to be returned. The red-haired steward handed back the keys without question, having held them for more than 40 days. Upon being interrogated by the lord of the manor as to who he was, Simon simply replied enigmatically that "he was begotten upon the wife of a local rustic by a demon who appeared in the form of her husband". And so Simon disappeared from Stackpole as suddenly as he had arrived.

Mr Noe comes to Letterston

Once upon a time, in the vicinity of Letterston, there was a lonely inn much used by travellers. Normally they were on their way from South Pembrokeshire, having passed through the Treffgarne Gorge on their way to Fishguard and the north coast. Most travellers who arrived at dusk were happy to stop the night in the inn rather than continue their journey, for the roads were not good and in the darkness and the wind and rain there were dangers for those who did not know the terrain. And there was another problem for the unwary traveller: a particularly sad and lonely female ghost which haunted the road nearby, wailing and crying out "The days are long and the nights are cold, waiting for Noe." Neither the innkeeper nor the other local people knew whose ghost it was, and nobody had heard of a Mr Noe.

Then, one dark winter night, when the wind was howling around the inn and the rain beating relentlessly on the roof, there was an urgent knocking on the door. The innkeeper opened up, and in came a dishevelled young man, soaked to the skin. He was a complete stranger, never before seen in the area. He took off his rainclothes and bowed stiffly to the assembled company. Then he gradually dried himself out in front of the blazing log fire, but he said not a word to anybody. At last he called for a drink and a meal, and the innkeeper and his regular customers watched as he ate in silence. His hands shook as he finished his meal, and all those present noticed the strange faraway look in his eyes.

At last the stranger rose to his feet, paid for his meal, and said that he must be on his way. The landlord was astonished. "But it is a terrible night outside," he said, "and the dark woods in the valley make it a fearsome place for travellers. Besides, there is a female ghost that haunts the road, who wails and cries that she waits for a man called Noe."

The young stranger looked the innkeeper in the eye as he pulled on his heavy coat. "I am the man that the ghost must meet," he said. And with that he rushed out into the wild storm.

The mysterious Mr Noe was never seen again. But strange to relate, neither was the sad ghost. Some of the locals thought that Mr Noe had deceived a young lady, who had died of a broken heart. Others said that Noe was a murderer unable to live with his terrible secret. But all agreed that justice had in the end been done, leaving the lonely road for other travellers to pass in peace.

Otherworldly Tale from Abercych

In the Celtic hero legends Arawn is the King of the Otherworld who changes places with Pwyll, Prince of Dyfed, in one of the famous stories of the Mabinogion. That particular story has as its focal point the deep wooded valley of Glyn Cych. It may be that in the Celtic mind the valley was considered to be a magical place where the gods and the heroes of the past came into contact with one another, just as they did at the magical mound at Narberth.

There is a strange story from a wealthy farmhouse not far from Abercych, which again seems to emphasize a link with the Otherworld. A large and respectable family lived in the farmhouse, and space was at a premium. However none of the family would use a certain upstairs room because it was haunted by a "troublesome spirit" which could often be heard crying out (in Welsh) in a loud voice "Long is the day, and long is the night, and long is waiting for Arawn". The family used the room as an occasional guest bedroom, but the family members were so frightened by its haunted atmosphere that they hardly dared to open the door and go inside, even in broad daylight.

One cold winter evening the members of the family were sitting around the fire waiting for their supper when a stranger knocked at the door of the house. He was welcomed inside and encouraged to come and warm himself by the fire. This he did, and he asked hesitantly if he could be given some food and a bed for the night. The farmer readily agreed to share supper with him, but explained that they could not offer him a bed since they had hardly enough beds for themselves and since every bedroom was occupied. "We have one other upstairs room," said the farmer. "But we are afraid that it is haunted by a most miserable ghost, and we don't dare to ask you to spend the night there."

At this the stranger looked not at all surprised, but begged to be allowed to sleep in the room. He said that he was sure that there was nothing in the room which could do him harm. "Very well," said the farmer reluctantly. "You are welcome to sleep there if you insist, although I certainly would not sleep there myself. We will make a bed up for you after supper." During supper the stranger appeared very tired and participated only reluctantly in the family's conversation. At last someone asked him his name and the family was amazed when he replied "Arawn", for that was the name of the King of the Otherworld and the name which was always called out in the haunted bedroom.

The farmer's wife made up the bed in the haunted room, and the stranger retired for the night. Strange to say there were no sounds from the room; nothing moved and no cries echoed around the house. When the family got up the next morning the farmer went up to the guest bedroom to call the stranger for breakfast and to enquire whether he had passed a comfortable night. Much to his surprise there was no trace of the man.

Furthermore the ghost was also gone, and from that day on the room was never again haunted or felt to be unpleasant in any way.

Haunted Houses

The Ghost at Little Milford

At Little Milford there is an old house down by the tidal Western Cleddau which has had its own resident ghost for many years. The ghost is reputed to be that of Caesar Mathias, who was a well-known pillar of the local establishment. In 1753 he obtained a long lease on the Little Milford estate, and later moved into the house with his wife Alice. He lived there with his family until about 1779, and since he filled prestigious posts (for example, he was both Mayor of Pembroke and High Sheriff of the county) the house was very much a part of the social scene for the Pembrokeshire gentry. He died in 1795.

In the 1800s the house was used as a rectory, and it was said to be haunted by the ghost of the old gentleman. Near the front door of the house there was a curtain, behind which a set of stone steps led down into the cellar. The ghost used to come up the steps and emerge from behind the curtain, and it was firmly believed by the servants in the house that he lived in an underground passage that led from the cellar under the river to "the old palace" on the opposite shore near Boulston. The story was that Caesar had encountered and killed a smuggler in the tunnel long, long ago, and that his ghost could not leave the scene of this terrible and traumatic incident. Whatever the truth of the matter, when the Rev Jackson Taylor was living in the house as rector, the haunting was so bad that he could not keep any servants. At last he had to perform an exorcism, reading from the prayer book and going round the house with bell, book and candle. And just to make sure, he chased the ghost around the house with a horse-whip! That apparently did the trick, and the haunting was much reduced; but later on, when the family of Mr Harcourt Roberts occupied the house after 1894, people were convinced that the ghost was still in the cellar.

There were unaccountable sounds, such as strange creaking sounds and footsteps walking across the yard and then simply stopping. Mrs Pauline Burdon spent her childhood at Little Milford, and was quite convinced of the presence of the ghost. She and her sister were too scared to go down into the cellar, but apparently their mother was not at all frightened by Caesar, and indeed quite enjoyed his company.

Ghosts at Bush House, near Pembroke

Bush House, not far from Pembroke, has long had the reputation of being one of the most haunted gentry houses in Pembrokeshire. It was once the home of the Meyrick family, one of whom was old John Meyrick, once the Chief Justice of South Wales. The locals were convinced that he was rewarded for his wicked ways by being carried off by the Devil, for his body seems to have disappeared under mysterious circumstances. At any rate his ghost, in the form of a dignified old gentleman, has often been encountered in the house at night.

In 1955 there were a number of strange occurrences when three Irish workmen were employed on conversion work at Bush House. For a while the men slept in one of the rooms in the house, but no sooner had they moved in than they noticed a cold heavy atmosphere there during the hours of darkness. The Tilley lamp which they used in the room behaved in a very erratic way; at night there were bangings and rattling noises from the doors and walls; and the youngest of the workmen felt sharp tuggings on the overcoat which he used as a bed-cover. The three were so frightened that they bolted one of the doors into the room and closed the other one with battens and nails. But still the strange events continued.

On the second night the men refused to sleep in the same room and moved instead to a room on the top floor of the house. From the window of this room they observed, glowing in the moonlight, the figure of a lady dressed in a crinoline gown walking back and forth on the path outside.

The men fled from the house in the middle of the night and refused to sleep there again. During their flight two of the men were injured, and subsequently claimed compensation from their employers, much to the amusement of the national press.

On another occasion, after Bush House became a part of Bush School, a night watchman was doing his rounds outside the old building at 2 am when he suddenly encountered an elderly gentleman of medium build wearing breeches, leggings and an old shooting jacket. Under his arm he carried a double-barrelled sporting gun, and by his side were three dogs. The watchman spoke to the figure, first in English and then in Welsh, but he received no reply, and then the ghostly sportsman and his dogs walked off and disappeared into a small pond. The "old-fashioned" gentleman with his three dogs has also been seen by many other people from the area over the years.

One explanation of the phantom sportsman and the lady in the crinoline gown can be found in nineteenth-century local history. Apparently a gentleman of Bush House was out shooting one day with his dogs in the grounds, while his wife travelled into Pater (the old name for Pembroke Dock) in her coach. When she returned her husband met the coach on the way home, and as she opened the door to speak to him, the gun went off by accident. The lady was mortally wounded, and the poor man never recovered from the tragedy.

In recent years the house has been used as a home for elderly people. The eldest son of Mr David James works there as a care assistant. As a matter of routine, the local police call in now and then to check that all is well, and they have frequently reported that a light is on in one of the top floor rooms. On each occasion, a care assistant runs upstairs to the room in question, only to find the elderly residents fast asleep and the light off. At first the assistants assumed that one of the residents was playing games with them. But this has happened too often to be explained away as the work of a practical joker, and the strange feature of the case is that the room and the passage outside are always found by the care assistants to be bitterly cold, even when the central heating is full on. (A chill in the air is, of course, often associated with a ghostly presence.) At other times the room and passage are at the same temperature as the rest of the house.

Haunted House in Newport

A certain house in Newport was once occupied by Dr Davies, the local doctor, and his wife. The household was looked after by a very severe housekeeper. She ruled the place with such a rod of iron that the poor housemaid who worked under her went about her work in fear and trepidation, and it was reputed that even Dr Davies was scared of her.

Shortly after Dr Davies died, the old housekeeper died also. The doctor's widow continued to live in the big house for some years, and during that time there was no evidence of ghostly activity.

Later on a young local family moved into the house, and while renovation work was going on they lived in the attic (which was quite well appointed) for a while. This was where the old housekeeper had lived.

But the parents became very concerned that the children would just not go into the bathroom. At bath-time in the evenings they more or less had to force them to go in through the door. There was clearly something there that frightened them. After a very short time they sold the property, and it was bought by a couple from Newport (Gwent). The wife was absolutely delighted with the big house at first. She told all the neighbours that it was just the place she had always wanted. In no time the new owners embarked upon a further renovation programme, with new electrical work, central heating, new carpeting and new decorations. The house was furnished in lavish style from top to bottom.

Then the wife disappeared. When the neighbours began to ask where she was, it appeared that nothing untoward had happened to her, but she had suddenly taken against the house, and had moved away from the area. Shortly after this the owners moved all their furniture out and the house was again put on the market. No reason was given, but rumours started to circulate that the big house was haunted.

While the house was on the market the owners asked a local man to undertake some further electrical work. The house was empty at the time, and the electrician worked on several occasions quite late into the evening. One evening he was invited to a nearby house for a meal after he had finished work; and he related to his hosts the strange experiences he had been having in the empty rooms and uncarpeted corridors. On a number of occasions he had felt that he was being watched, and more than once he felt the hair rising on the back of his neck. Once he had been so convinced that there was somebody there that he had called out and searched the house from top to bottom to find out who it was. He found nothing.

Neighbours who are old enough to remember old Dr Davies and his ferocious housekeeper are now convinced that the old lady has never really left the property. When the house is quiet, she rests in peace, but when there is noise and laughter, or when major alterations are going on, she gets extremely angry, and makes it her business to show her disapproval ....

29

Haunted Inns and Hotels

Castle Hotel, Little Haven

One of the best known of the haunted hostelries in Pembrokeshire is the Castle Hotel in Little Haven. A number of visitors have had strange and eerie experiences there. In 1972 Mr and Mrs Ash were asleep in their bedroom when Mrs Ash awoke with a start and listened to heavy footsteps approaching the bedroom. In the darkness she heard the bedroom door-handle being turned. Then, as she lay with her eyes wide open, and transfixed with fear, she heard someone, or something, opening the door and walking across the room towards the bed. She distinctly heard the floorboards creaking. Then the ghostly presence turned round, walked back across the creaking floorboards, and left the room. The door was quietly closed, and all returned to normal.

Next morning Mrs Ash told her husband what she had experienced, and they examined the floorboards, only to discover that they did not creak at all. Later they talked to John Gibson, the landlord, and he told them that the floorboards in their room creaked very badly until a few years previously, when he had had the floor re-laid. He also confirmed that various other guests had encountered a ghostly visitor in that particular room; but all agreed that he was perfectly harmless. Mr and Mrs Ash stayed in the same room for several more nights, and experienced nothing unusual.

Old Castle Inn, Narberth

There is a long tradition of hauntings in the old Castle Inn in Narberth. Perhaps this is not surprising, since the ruined castle is not far away, and castles are almost always inhabited by ghosts. Maybe the castle ghosts move into nearby inns where conditions are much warmer and a lot less draughty?

In 1982 Mr and Mrs Mel Taylor took over the inn and experienced a number of strange incidents, which confirmed in their minds tales about the building being haunted. A previous landlady had seen a ghostly figure dressed in a monk's habit, and in the early 1980s doors would suddenly open or close, lights would be turned off and on, and sometimes the beer coolers would be turned off in the middle of the night. One evening a neighbour, Mr Hughie John, saw a "tall man in a waistcoat" standing next to Mrs Mary Tyler behind the bar. She was quite unaware of the presence of anybody.

The most bizarre incidents occurred when a young couple were occupying a room on the second floor. In the middle of the night the young man, named Adam, got up to visit the bathroom. He returned to bed and was half asleep when the door burst open, even though it had been fastened on a latch. Then he saw his cigarettes, matches and car keys suddenly flip over as they lay on top of the record player at the bedside. Next day the lights went out of their own accord while he was in the bathroom. Mr and Mrs Tyler moved out of the inn after 3 months, but they claimed that the ghosts were not at all troublesome, and that family reasons lay behind the move. Sadly, the inn was abandoned before the turn of the century.

Phantom Ships

Those who study ghosts find it quite easy to explain how the spirits of human beings or even animals can "materialize" or manifest themselves after death. Living things are, after all, endowed with a life force or energy which can be measured in a variety of ways; and it is reasonable to assume that after the death of the physical body some of this life force may remain behind in the form of a "spirit" or shade. Things get more interesting (and a great deal more mysterious) when it comes to the ghostly reappearances of inanimate objects. Ghosts have been known to carry keys or books, and they are almost always fully dressed. Some who have encountered ghosts describe their footwear and headwear. There are records of ghostly carriages pulled by ghostly horses, and ghostly weapons carried by ghostly armies. But what are we to make of whole ships which appear as phantoms? There are two strange tales from Pembrokeshire which are very difficult to understand.

An old painting of Castle Pill in the nineteenth century

Strange Happening at Castle Pill, Milford

Around the year 1800, when the town of Milford was young, a wealthy wine merchant called John Warlow lived in Castle Hall. This magnificent mansion looked down on the shore of Castle Pill to the east of the town, and Mr Warlow made a habit of taking walks along the banks of the creek.

One fine summer's night he was walking home along the beach and enjoying the bright moonlight and the fresh breeze from the Haven. Suddenly he heard the unmistakable sound of a boat coming up the creek, which surprised him since the tide was out and the mudbanks were exposed in the moonlight. He could see no sign of a boat. The sounds continued, coming inexorably towards him. He heard the measured dip of oars in the water, the creaking of the rowlocks and the murmur of the bow wave.

Presently he heard the sound of the keel scraping on the gravelly beach by the side of the old quay wall, and then the sound of heavy feet on the steps of the quay. Still he saw nothing.

Greatly alarmed by this strange occurrence, Mr Warlow hurried back up the hill to Castle Hall, and related the incident to his family. He told of the sounds he had heard, and also described the strange stillness which had surrounded him, as if all of the normal noises of a summer's night had been blotted out while the sounds of the phantom boat continued.

A few days later an East Indiaman put into Milford for the purpose of repairs and anchored off shore. While it was there the mate died on board, and when the tide was sufficiently high his body in its coffin was brought ashore by rowing boat and landed in Castle Pill. The sailors beached their boat adjacent to the old quay and carried the coffin up the steps. Mr Warlow witnessed this event, and he observed that all of the sounds associated with it were exactly as he had heard them during his eerie experience in the moonlight.

Ghostly Pirate Ship at Tenby

On a dark midwinter afternoon in about 1558, in the reign of Queen Elizabeth the First, the people of Tenby saw a strange vessel sweeping across Carmarthen Bay. Driven by storm-force winds and mighty waves from the east, it was obviously out of control, with broken masts and spars, and shredded sails. As it came closer and closer to the shore, the people could see that it was unmanned, but there were strange lights and "spirit-forms" on the deck, and word soon spread that this was a phantom ship, or at least a solid ship populated by phantoms.

As darkness fell, the people could just make out the shape of the ship close inshore as she foundered upon a sand-bank close to the North Beach. Throughout the pitch-black night the people heard wailing and other strange ghostly sounds, as a result of which those living close to the beach had very little sleep.   At first light the storm had calmed, and the townspeople went down to the shore to search for the shipwreck. But there was not a trace of the ghostly vessel -- no timbers or rigging, no barrels, no strips of sail, no flotsam or jetsam of any sort. But upon the sand lay a man dressed in strange clothes, half drowned and unconscious.   The people pulled him clear of the waves and managed to revive him, and for a few days he stayed in the town as he was nursed back to health.   But he was a strange fellow, unwilling to talk about himself or even to give his name to those who would be his friends, and at last he moved out to live on the rocks of St Catherine's Island, which was cut off from the town with every high tide.

One day a local shepherd heard about the sailor's hermit-like existence on the island, and went across at low tide with some food and clothes. The man was grateful, and over the days and weeks that followed the shepherd went across to bring him food whenever he came in to Tenby to visit the town market. The sailor seemed to spend his time sitting on a crag gazing out to sea, with the seabirds wheeling about him. On each visit the shepherd begged the sailor to abandon his bleak and joyless existence and to go home with him, but the stranger always refused courteously.

St Catherine's Island, Tenby -- the temporary home for the strange man from the phantom pirate ship in 1558. The fort came much later.

Then at last, one stormy day when the waves were crashing against the seaward side of the little island, the stranger opened his heart to the shepherd. In a torrent of words he talked of his former life as a pirate, and he related how, in a fit of jealousy, he had murdered the woman who loved

33

him most. He said that all his comrades had perished on his ship, which was then manned by ghosts while driven by the storm onto the sands of the town's North Beach. At times, he said, as he sat upon the cliffs facing out to sea, sea maidens came and beckoned to him, calling out that his girl was happy and at rest.

Suddenly, as a great foam-crested wave rolled in towards the cliff where the two men were sitting, the pirate stood up in a highly agitated state. He pointed at the wave and shouted "I come. I come. Receive me, blest spirits!" And before the shepherd could stop him he leaped from the clifftop into the surging foam and was immediately lost to view. The horrified shepherd could do nothing, and returned to the mainland alone. The pirate's body was never found.

Ghosts on the Highway

Phantom at Cosheston

One night in January 1994 thirteen-year-old Gavin Roche was playing football with some friends in a Cosheston street, outside Pendine House. It was a cold, still night, and the children were playing beneath the street lights. Gavin took a break from the game, and as he stood on the pavement he glanced down the road. There he saw something he had never seen before, and has no wish to see again.

Suddenly, running out of the darkness, there came a tall faceless figure. "It was very tall," said Gavin afterwards, "like a skinny shadow, a silhouette, about 100 yards away. Within seconds it had covered the distance between us. I could see it, but I couldn't hear it, and there was nobody there. It was sort of floating towards me, but it was very fast. There was no wind that night, but its long hair was moving wildly as it sped past."

Gavin was the only one to see the phantom, but he became so scared that he shouted to his friends to run, and they all ran home as fast as their legs could carry them. After a while they decided to return to the street to investigate, and, if possible, to continue their game of football. But it was obvious that the phantom was still there, and this time a friend named Matthew Weidemann experienced a very strong sense of its presence. The boys ran away again, and this time stayed at home, trembling and feeling very scared. Gavin's mother Jacqueline quickly saw that he was very frightened indeed.

Afterwards one of the parents told the story to a local newspaper, and the publicity encouraged others to talk. It transpired that two of Gavin's other friends had also seen the faceless phantom a few weeks before. They had said nothing at the time because they were quite convinced that nobody would believe them.

The Headless Phantoms at Sampson Cross

In the latter part of the last century one of the ghosts of Stackpole Court was known locally as "Lady Mathias". She was headless, and was often seen riding by in her carriage, accompanied by a headless coachman and drawn by two headless horses. According to tradition the phantom journeys were always made between Tenby and Sampson Cross, via Stackpole Court. Some of the locals used to say that the ghost was really that of Jane Mansell of Muddlescwm, whose memorial is in St Petrox Church.

Many attempts were made to rid the area of this headless old lady, but no exorcism was successful until the Vicar of St Petrox doomed her to empty Bosherston Lily Ponds with a cockle-shell as a ladle. She must have found this task somewhat daunting. In a fit of pique she refused to keep her part of the bargain, and drove off in her coach into the ether, never to be seen again at Sampson Cross or anywhere else.

The Fighting Ghosts at Holloway Bridge, near Tenby

In 1721-22 one Thomas Athoe was mayor of Tenby. One day he travelled to Wiston Fair, and while there he became involved in a fierce quarrel about some cattle with a cousin of his called George Marchant. There was already bad blood between them because George had married a girl with whom Athoe's son had been passionately in love. So following the quarrel father and son decided to murder George Marchant.

The conspirators laid in wait for their intended victim one day near the bridge over the Marsh Stream (Holloway Bridge). When he appeared they killed him in a bloody and ferocious confrontation. The murderers were caught and charged, causing great excitement in the town especially since one of the accused was the mayor. They were found guilty of the horrible crime, and were taken to London in chains. There the two of them were unceremoniously hanged.

But for over a century afterwards the ghosts of the three men (murderers and victim) still carried on their fierce and terrible fight under the old bridge, to the great annoyance of the people of Tenby.

The old bridge has long since given way to the main road between Penally and Tenby, but in certain light conditions you can still see the wraiths moving about on the marshes.

Ghostly Humour

The Incompetent Ghost at Crymych

Once upon a time a family moved into an old house near Crymych, and found that it had a resident ghost. The ghost, whose name was Gwilym, appeared to be that of an old man, and he would turn up quite frequently in the house, making strange noises, pushing over chairs, walking through closed doors and doing various other ghostly things. However, he was not a very good ghost since he was obviously quite harmless and since he appeared far too frequently for his own good; so the family started to take him for granted, and even the children laughed at him instead of screaming with terror as children are supposed to do. This made the poor ghost quite miserable, and he began to waste away until he was but a shadow of his former self.

At last the family became so worried about Gwilym that they decided to take the matter in hand. So next time he appeared the father said to him "Now then, Gwilym, we are getting very worried about you. Come in and sit down here in the living room and we will have a little chat." The old ghost looked surprised at this invitation, but reluctantly agreed, and then came in and sat on the old sofa. The mother looked him in the eye and told him that he wasn't being taken seriously enough, and that he would make a far better job of being a ghost if he did his haunting occasionally rather than all the time. Then young Dafydd piped up and said "Why don't you just come back and haunt us every seven years? Then, when you knock things over and walk through the wall or something we will all have forgotten about you and we will be quite scared! And you will feel really pleased with yourself, just like a proper ghost."

The family all thought this an excellent idea, and after giving the matter some thought Gwilym had to admit it was worth trying. So there and then they all made a deal. Gwilym would appear and do a good haunting in seven years' time, and then when they had all recovered from the shock they would sit down for a chat and renegotiate a new deal.

Then Gwilym, true to his word, disappeared through the closed door with a final moan, and did not reappear for seven whole years.

When he came again he popped up through the floor quite unexpectedly and did a splendid haunting, which gave all the members of the family a thoroughly good fright. Afterwards they all sat down and agreed that things had gone very smoothly indeed, and Gwilym and the family renewed the agreement by mutual consent. And so it was that old Gwilym appeared quite regularly, every seventh year, as long as the family and their descendants occupied the house. The arrangement is still working well after almost 200 years, and we may imagine that the old ghost is now enjoying life to the full, and looking far better for it.

36

Chapter Three: Phantom Funerals

There are many tales in Pembrokeshire concerning fetches or phantom funerals which were always held to be portents of real events. In Welsh the word "toili" is used for a phantom funeral. Generally the observer of a phantom funeral sees a throng of people following a hearse, and sometimes he or she is jostled or caught up in the crush of people. It is perfectly normal for the observer to recognize those involved in the funeral procession, and even to communicate with them. After the sighting of a phantom funeral a death occurs, and the real funeral procession reproduces in exact detail the supernatural procession experienced by the observer.

There are some variations on the theme, including one story of a phantom funeral oration, and one of a phantom coffin. The best known local tale concerns Holloway Farm near Penally, but similar stories come from all over the county. The stories are extremely difficult for "ghost hunters" to explain, for they involve manifestations of spirit energy before a death occurs. (Normally a ghost or spirit is assumed to represent the residue of a person's life-force left behind after death.)

John Salmon and the Toili at Llanycefn

Llanycefn is a small hamlet in one of the tributary valleys of the Eastern Cleddau. The countryside round about has deep valleys and much woodland. There is a bellcote church, rebuilt around 1904. This story relates to the mid-1800s, when the old church was still in use. An old man named John Salmon was going about his business one day, in broad daylight, when he was surprised to see a funeral procession going along the road towards the church. He was not aware that any of his neighbours had died, so he suspected that he was watching a phantom funeral or "toili". He looked closely at the line of mourners, and recognized most of those present. However, he was surprised to see that there was no vicar at the head of the procession.

Unknown to Mr Salmon, the vicar of Llanycefn had been called away to his home town to deal with some family crisis, and did not return until a couple of weeks had passed. So it was that when a neighbour died a few days later the funeral procession passed along the same roadway, exactly as foreseen by Mr Salmon. All the neighbours were there, including Mr Salmon himself, walking in exactly the order foreseen. And there was no vicar at the head of the procession, since a minister from another parish had agreed to meet the procession at the church in order to conduct the funeral service.

Phantom Funeral at Glandwr

In the early 1800s there was a well-known parson in the Glandwr area called Rev John Griffiths. He preached from many pulpits in the chapels of the eastern part of Pembrokeshire against the prevailing belief in the "canwyll gorff" or corpse candle and the "toili" or phantom funeral.

One night he was involved in a "remarkable circumstance". It was a pitch black night, and he was returning home on horseback along a dark and narrow lane. Suddenly his mare reared up, as if frightened by something in her path. Rev Griffiths could neither see nor sense anything, and urged his horse on. But the mare went once more to the side of the lane and would not continue. So the minister spurred the horse and took his whip to her; but immediately she leaped straight over the hedge and into a field. The reverend gentleman then dismounted and led the mare back to the lane, by now feeling somewhat nervous himself.

He strained his ears so as to discover what had frightened the horse, and gradually he became aware that he could hear heavy footsteps coming towards him. Closer and closer they came, and he realized that this was the sound of a great procession involving many people. As they went past he managed to keep his horse under control; and then, feeling inquisitive and having also got his nerves under control, he determined to follow the phantom procession. This he did, and after a while he realized that this was a "toili" on its way to his own chapel graveyard in Glandwr. The procession went into the graveyard and stopped in a part where there were previously no graves. After much shuffling of feet on the grass, the sounds disappeared. The minister saw nothing, but heard a great deal.

Within a few days of this experience, one of the chapel congregation died. The large funeral procession, with the Rev Griffiths at its head, passed along the same lane as the "toili" had done, and stopped in exactly the same place in the graveyard, where a fresh grave had been dug for receiving the body in its coffin. After this, the minister was never again heard to ridicule the local belief in phantom funerals and other supernatural things, and it was clear that he had been profoundly affected by his strange experience.

Rhys Bach in Cwm Cych

Once upon a time a carpenter named Rhys Thomas lived in Capel Iwan. He was a good carpenter and a thoughtful and sensible sort of man. One night he was walking home along a country lane not far from Capel Iwan, in the valley of Cwm Cych. He had just crossed over the bridge of Pont Wedwst, and after passing the chapel near the river, he was climbing up the hill through the woods towards the village. It was a dark night, and although the lane was overhung by tall trees Rhys could just about see where he was going.

Then he became aware of voices, and made out the sounds of shuffling feet coming towards him. The voices grew louder and louder, but Rhys could see no lanterns in the darkness, nor could he make out any human figures in the dim light. He pressed on, and at last felt that he was in the midst of a throng of people, although he could still see nothing.

He realized that he was encountering a "toili" or phantom funeral. He did not feel particularly afraid, and concluded that he was among people he knew. Then he felt an unseen hand upon his shoulder, and a female voice said to him "Good day to you, Rhys bach, how are you?" Then the invisible procession passed him by and continued down the steep hill towards the chapel.

Rhys said nothing of his encounter and awaited developments. A month later, on a winter's afternoon when it was still daylight, Rhys was walking the same way home, up the hill of Rhiw Edwst, when he met a funeral procession coming down the hill towards him. The sounds were exactly those he had heard before. He recognized many of those in the procession, and he took off his cap and acknowledged them as they passed.

As the main part of the throng passed him in the narrow lane a woman whom he knew put her hand upon his shoulder. "Good day to you, Rhys bach," she said. "How are you?" And the procession went on its way.

Strange Event at Holloway Farm, Penally

On a winter's evening around 1850 an employee of the Vicar of Penally saw a large phantom funeral procession near Holloway Farm, and he recognized several neighbours among the mourners. The Vicar laughed at the man when told about this, and showed even greater scepticism when told that the phantom funeral had left the road, passing over a hedge bank into an adjacent field and then returning to the road a hundred yards or so further along. The Vicar continued to express his doubts, adding "If this has indeed happened, you must surely be able to show me the place, since the hedge will be all trampled down." So the man took the Vicar to the place, but there was no sign of trampling or any other disturbance.

Shortly after this there was a spell of severe winter weather, with heavy snowfall, during which Mr Williams, the tenant of Holloway Farm, died. On its way to the church the funeral party found the narrow lane blocked by snow, and the coffin was carried over the hedge bank at precisely the spot crossed by the phantom funeral some days earlier. All the mourners followed, and the funeral procession walked along the edge of the field, eventually returning to the lane in precisely the spot foreseen in the "fetch funeral".

Toili at Felin Cilgwyn

The Davies family of Felin Cilgwyn, near Newport, were reputed to have had the gift of second sight, and around the year 1905 Miss Martha Davies told how her mother had seen the phantom of her own funeral before she died. The old lady was out walking down the lane from Caersalem Chapel to Felin Cilgwyn one night when she was terrified by a phantom funeral procession coming up the hill towards her. Although the lane is very narrow at that point, the funeral passed her by, and she noticed that the Vicar of Pontfaen, Rev Jenkin Evans, was walking behind the procession. This was unusual, for there would normally be no reason for a minister of the Church in Wales to be attending a funeral in the Baptist Chapel of Caersalem. When Mrs Davies returned home, greatly shaken by the episode, she described the Vicar's clothes in detail, and made special mention of his hat.

The very next day old Mrs Davies was taken seriously ill, and before long she was dead. Everybody in the neighbourhood believed that she had seen an apparition of her own funeral. She belonged to Caersalem Chapel herself, and plans were put in hand for the funeral.

Her daughter Martha was at that time a maidservant at Pontfaen Vicarage, and the Vicar felt it his duty to accompany the girl to the funeral. He drove her from Pontfaen in his carriage, and left the pony and trap at the Pen-y-Bont inn, just up the road, since there was very little room at Felin Cilgwyn. He accompanied Martha to the house of mourning on foot, and later followed the funeral procession along the lane to Caersalem Chapel, again on foot. Martha later said that the scene -- even down to the Vicar's clothes and hat - was exactly as her mother had described from her vision a few days before her death.

The Railway Porter at Llanychaer

During October 1905 a young porter who worked for the GWR near Cardiff came home ill to Llanychaer, in the Gwaun Valley. His condition caused great concern in the family. Dafydd, a young friend of his who lived nearby, sat up with him all night to keep him company; but at about 3 am the patient became so poorly that the lad decided to fetch his father, who lived in a small cottage down the road.

As soon as Dafydd set foot outside the door he was astonished to find that he was in the midst of a large crowd of people. He noticed a coffin resting on two chairs, ready to be placed on a bier, and concluded that this must be a funeral party ready to move off to the church. When Dafydd attempted to walk down the road towards the cottage where his friend's father lived, the procession moved in the same direction, and he was caught up in the crowd. He was swept along as far as the old man's cottage, where he struggled to free himself.   He hammered on the door, but was so frightened that he almost passed out before it was opened.

Only three days later the young railway porter died, and the events surrounding the funeral were exactly as Dafydd had foreseen, with the coffin resting on two chairs, the great throng of mourners, and the procession passing along the road towards Llanychaer Church.

Fetch Funeral at St David's

Mr Pavin Phillips had a good friend who was a clergyman in St David's. One of his parishioners was an old woman called Molly who frequently observed phantom funerals.   After church she would say to him "Ay ay, Reverend bach, you'll be here of a weekday soon, for I saw a funeral last night."   And her predictions were always fulfilled.

However, the clergyman remained sceptical, and on one occasion he asked her "Well, Molly, have you seen a funeral lately?"   "Ay,ay, Reverend bach," came the reply. "I saw one a night or two ago. But there's a strange thing. You did something I never seen before."

"Why, what was that?" inquired the minister.

"Well, as you met up with the procession you stooped down and picked something up off the ground."

"Fancy that," thought the clergyman to himself. "I'll try you out this time, Molly, and see if I can't make a liar of you for once."

Some time afterwards the clergyman was summoned to a funeral at a nearby village. He arrived on horseback, and as he dismounted to meet the mourners he caught his surplice in his spur and in the ensuing tangle dropped some possessions onto the ground. As he bent down to pick them up a picture of old Molly entered his mind, with a sly smile on her face ....

Fetch Funeral at Carew

Around the year 1880 a nonconformist minister from Carew invited a colleague (who was also a reverend gentleman) from a neighbouring village to pay him a visit. He was due to act as guest preacher in the village chapel on the following day, and the local minister booked a bedroom for his guest above a little shop. He arrived safely enough, but being an elderly man who was not in the best of health he decided to retire to bed nice and early.

Downstairs the shopkeeper was making up his books after the week's trading when he was terrified to see two carpenters (whom he recognized) coming downstairs from the bedroom carrying a coffin. Without saying a word they opened the front door, carried their burden out of the shop, and disappeared. The poor shopkeeper was so frightened that he hardly slept a wink that night, and in the morning, when his guest came downstairs, he related what he had seen. They were discussing the possibility that this might have been a "fetch funeral" when the local minister came to see his friend. So the shopkeeper narrated the strange tale all over again, at which the new arrival uttered a strange cry, threw up his hands and staggered backwards.

Before the guest and the shopkeeper could do anything the minister collapsed "in a fit of apoplexy". The two men immediately carried him upstairs and laid him down on the bed which had been occupied in the night by his friend. And there he died, before they could send a message for the local doctor. Although it was now a Sunday, the doctor came along and confirmed that the minister was dead, and the village undertaker was asked to make arrangements. Later in the day two carpenters arrived, bearing a coffin. They were the same two carpenters seen by the shopkeeper in his vision. They put the body inside, carried the burden downstairs, opened the door of the shop, and went outside en route to the minister's own house. Everything that happened was exactly as foreseen by the shopkeeper the previous evening.

Visitation at Thornton

In 1859 there was great excitement in the town of Milford, for the new railway was almost complete. Gangs of navvies were working on the line, and many of them were billeted out in local farms and cottages. Many of the workers were Irish. They worked hard and drank hard, and they remained happy so long as ale was in plentiful supply at the end of a long day's toil with picks and shovels.

A number of the Irish navvies had their lodgings in a farmhouse close to the route of the line, in the hamlet of Thornton. One evening they were enjoying a "noson lawen" (merry night) with their Welsh hosts and with a number of their friends from other lodging houses. The ale was flowing generously. Welsh and Irish tales were told, and many a fine old song was sung. When the merriment was at its height, the dogs in the yard suddenly began to bark and howl for no apparent reason. A hush fell over the company in the farmhouse as the dogs' howls subsided to frightened whimpers. Then everybody heard a shuffling noise at the front door, followed by a furious knocking. This was unusual, since the front door of the farmhouse was kept locked while all the daily comings and goings were through the back door. At first nobody moved, but then one of the Irishmen leapt to his feet and said "Who would be after knocking at your front door at this time of night? I will go and see who it is." But the farmer felt that all was not well, and replied "No, no, Eamonn bach, stay here. Bide awhile, and let us listen." So Eamonn returned to his chair.

Then there was the sound of shuffling feet going slowly along the front passage. The parlour door was heard to open, and there was more shuffling of feet. Then something heavy was set on the parlour table with a thump. The heavy footsteps were heard going back down the passage to the front door, and then everything became quiet again. The farmer and his family and guests were all frightened by this strange episode. But Eamonn, having had a few too many, was keen to investigate, and after picking up a rushlight he went into the parlour, followed by two of his friends. They could see no sign of the phantom visitors, and everything in the parlour was just as normal. There were no footprints, and the front door was locked and bolted, just as usual. Everybody was mystified, and there was much speculation as to the meaning of the strange visitation. But now the spirit had gone out of the party, so the guests went home and the residents all went to bed.

Next morning there was an accident down on the railway line. Eamonn the Irishman was killed, and since the farmhouse was so close to the line his workmates carried his body on an old door up the hill from the railway cutting. On reaching the farm they knocked frantically on the front door. When it was opened they shuffled slowly inside, along the passage and into the parlour. And there, with difficulty, they lifted Eamonn's battered body on its makeshift stretcher onto the table. Then they trudged out again, with bowed heads, into the daylight. As they went the farmer's hair stood on end, for he realised that all the sounds made by the men were exactly the same as those of the previous night.

Phantom Funeral in St Katherine's Church

Mr John Pavin Phillips was a well-known businessman who had a strong interest in the supernatural. One of his intriguing tales is as follows. Around 1810 his grandfather had a strange experience along with seven or eight other members of his family.

They all lived near Castle Pill. One fine summer evening they were all sitting outside the front door, enjoying the evening sun, when they saw a funeral procession approaching St Katherine's Churchyard. A coffin was borne aloft on the shoulders of six strong men, and it was followed by a crowd of mourners along the pathway to the church. There it was met by the parson, whom the observers all recognized. The parson led the procession into the church, and after a while they all came out again and the burial ceremony was completed in the corner of the churchyard.

Grandfather Phillips and his family were astonished by this strange occurrence, since they were pillars of the community and would certainly have been aware of any death in the town and any planned funeral in the church. One of the family members ran over to the church to ask who had been buried, but returned after a while to report that there had been no burial that day. They all concluded that they had seen a fetch funeral; and sure enough, a few days later a neighbour died and was buried in the churchyard just where the ghostly funeral had been seen.

43

Ghostly Burial
in City Road
Cemetery,
Haverfordwest

In September 1978, 13-year old Jane Evans of Hawthorn Rise in Haverfordwest was going off to bed and went to the window to draw her bedroom curtains. She glanced outside as she did so, and saw down below, very clearly, in the City Road cemetery, several people standing around a grave. She was so frightened that she screamed and fell sobbing onto her bed. Mr and Mrs Evans rushed upstairs to see what the matter was. Jane told them she had seen strangely dressed people in the cemetery.

Shadowy figures in the City Road Cemetery, Haverfordwest. Actually these are just ivy-covered headstones.....

Mrs Evans looked out and saw a group of ghostly figures at the grave of her husband's grandparents. Most of the people were bending down over the grave, but one very tall man was standing up. She saw him very clearly, dressed in black clothing and with a high stiff collar and large top hat. "He looked very much like an old-fashioned minister or undertaker", said Mrs Evans. Her husband thought that somebody must be playing some sort of prank, so went to the cemetery to investigate. There was no sign of anybody and no traces of foot marks on the grass. The family members were quite convinced that they had witnessed a ghostly funeral "replay" involving one of Mr Evans's grandparents.

44

Small Coffin in Llanddewi Velfrey

In the month of April 1875, Billy Thomas the postman was out walking in his garden near the village of Llanddewi Velfrey. It was quite late and very dark, but it was a beautiful starlit night and there was enough light for Billy to see where he was going. He had some family trouble on his mind, and he was deep in thought. At last he decided that he should return to the house, and as he turned he saw a man immediately in front of him on top of the hedge. The man appeared to have a strange wooden object beside him. He stood for a moment on the hedge bank as if he was resting, and then he picked the wooden object up and placed it on his shoulder. Then he came down off the hedge, and crossed the garden by an old public footpath which was still used by some of the older local people. As Billy watched, the man crossed over a stile on the other side of the garden and disappeared. Before he vanished from sight Billy realized that the wooden object was a small white coffin.

A few days later a child in a neighbouring family sickened very suddenly with epilepsy and died. Strange to say, the carpenter from Llanddewi Velfrey brought the coffin to the house along exactly the same footpath, resting on the hedge-bank for a moment, crossing the garden and then climbing over the stile on the opposite hedge. Billy happened to be in the garden at the time. Every movement made by the carpenter was identical to that observed by Billy in his strange vision. The only difference was that on this occasion Billy exchanged a few words with the carpenter before he went on his way.

Accident at Cold Blow

A well known squire who lived close to Tenby was travelling home by coach from the railway station at Narberth. He had been away from home for some time, and he had been met at the station by his coachman and his carriage and horses. The coachman was accompanied by a friend who sat with him in front, and the squire sat inside the coach.

As the coach and horses went along the road close to the hamlet of Cold Blow the coachman and his friend saw something which they described as a "black mass" moving towards them. It was a very dark evening, and the shapes ahead of them were very indistinct. But as they came closer, they perceived that they were looking at a funeral. The horses became restless, and then they were struck by panic, plunging and rearing and soon becoming uncontrollable. In the pandemonium the carriage was overturned, and the horses escaped from their harnesses and bolted into the distance. The coachman and his friend were thrown over a hedge into an adjacent field, from which they later emerged bruised and battered and covered with mud. The squire who was inside the overturned coach was shaken but not otherwise injured.

45

The three men were convinced that they had seen a phantom funeral, and certainly the behaviour of the horses had been quite out of character, for they were not normally frightened by crowds of people passing close to them. The squire later ascertained that there had been no funeral passing along the road on that date or at that time. The three were greatly shaken by their experience, but were afraid that they would encounter disbelief and even derision if they told the story to anyone else. They agreed on a mundane explanation of the accident, and it was only after the passage of a number of years that they admitted what had really happened on that dark evening at Cold Blow.

Phantom Funeral in East Street, Newport

In the middle part of the last century, William Havard owned a small shop in Newport and lived at a cottage called Penybanc. One night, having had various jobs to do after closing the shop, he was returning home very late. As he walked along East Street, he was surprised to hear the sounds of wailing and weeping ahead of him. He stopped and listened, and suddenly he felt himself pushed backwards, as if by a large crowd of people. He could do nothing about it, but he was pushed along and jostled about until he came to a wider part of the road. There the crush became less intense, and he was able to extricate himself from the "phantom crowd". He pressed himself against the hedge at the side of the road and became aware of a "toili" or phantom funeral procession going past him. He saw the coffin, recognized most of the mourners, and heard the women sobbing. What is more, he saw and recognized the local minister; and then he was even more surprised to see himself in the procession.

Much shaken by this experience, William hurried home and told his wife and two or three of his neighbours about it. Exactly a fortnight later, a man called Owen Griffith of Pencnwc died, and the funeral procession had a long walk into town. The mourners walked down Berry Hill, over the old bridge at Pen-y-bont and into the town. As the procession passed along East Street it was identical in every respect to that observed a fortnight earlier by William Havard.

There are other stories of phantom funerals in Pembrokeshire, but they do not differ greatly from the tales told above. However, there are some very unusual episodes recorded in old newspapers and books. One concerns a Mr John Llewelyn of Rhydwilym, who heard himself giving a funeral oration for a man not yet dead, and there is a strange tale from Cresswell Quay about a phantom funeral which was headed by a bright light. Also, I have encountered a hilarious tale about an inebriated farmer and a pair of coffin-carrying phantoms at Pont Clegyr, St David's.

46

Chapter Four: Corpse Candles

The corpse candle ("canwyll gorff") was said to be a sign, particularly in the diocese of St David's, of a forthcoming death. It would take the form of a light passing along the route to be followed by a funeral, or hovering around the spot where a death would occur, where an accident might take place, or where a coffin might be interred in sanctified ground. If the death omen took the form of a falling light it would be called a "tanwedd". In 1888 Edward Laws stated that St Daniel's Cemetery in Pembroke was a particularly fine place for seeing corpse candles! There are records of sightings of the corpse candle in quite recent times, but most of the surviving Pembrokeshire stories are from the last century.

Corpse Candle near Tenby

This story comes from Tenby. One night a young schoolmistress was lodging in a farmhouse near the town. She was lying awake in the pitch darkness when she noticed a small light appear near the doorway. She later described it as being "like a little star". The light moved towards her bed, then stopped and lowered itself to her feet. She was terrified, and when she realized that nobody was carrying the light she screamed and woke up the rest of the household. They ran to her room to find out what had happened, and could do nothing but try to console her. She would not remain in the room, but eventually she went off to sleep in another bedroom and the incident was forgotten.

Six weeks later the young teacher went off on holiday. While she was away the farmer's wife, who had been a strong and healthy woman, was suddenly taken ill. Although she was expected to recover she deteriorated rapidly and died. The young schoolmistress was informed, and she hurried back just in time for the funeral. When she arrived she was taken to the room which she had previously occupied -- and there she saw the body of the farmer's wife laid out exactly where she had seen the corpse candle.

Canwyll Gorff in Cwm Gwaun

In the early 1800s Mr Morris Griffiths was first a schoolmaster and then minister of Jabes Baptist Chapel at Pontfaen in the Gwaun Valley. One night he was returning home from Tredafydd when he saw a large red light over a section of the roadway not far from Llanychllwydog Church. He had heard about corpse candles, and assumed that this must be one, so being an educated and inquisitive man he watched with great interest to see what might happen next. The "canwyll gorff" stood still over exactly the same spot on the road for about a quarter of an hour, and then, still as bright as ever, it moved into the church. Later it came out again and hovered over a spot in the churchyard. Then it disappeared.

A few days later, while Mr Griffiths was in school with the children, he heard a great noise overhead, and thought that the school roof was collapsing. He ran outside to investigate, but saw nothing. Next day, one of his pupils, the son of a Mr Higgon of Pontfaen, took to his bed with a mysterious illness. A few days later the little boy died. When the carpenter came to fetch the boards for the coffin he had to climb up into the attic to fetch them, and while handling them he made a noise just like that which the schoolmaster had heard in school. Before the funeral took place there was a spell of very heavy rainfall, but the event went off more or less as planned. However, when the funeral procession was making its way to the church the roadway was flooded, and the passage of the coffin and mourners was delayed for some time while those who had boots assisted others across the flooded area. This episode took a quarter of an hour, and occurred exactly where Mr Griffiths had observed the light hovering. Then the procession went into the church, and later the boy was buried in exactly that part of the churchyard indicated by the corpse candle ten days before.

An old photo of Jabes Chapel, probably dating from pre-1900

The Walton West Corpse Candle

In 1899 an old man from Walton West related that, when he was a boy, he and his younger brother were in bed one night, pinching one another and generally fooling about (as boys will) before going to sleep. Suddenly he saw a peculiar light on the bed. He stopped his horseplay and drew his brother's attention to it; but the other child could see nothing. He then hit the light with his hand, upon which it "went into a thousand fragments" before reforming into its original shape. Then the light gradually disappeared. Some days later a visitor to the house was given the boy's bedroom to sleep in, and died during the night just where the corpse candle had been seen.

Canwyll Gorff in Jabes Churchyard

Hettie Howells was a remarkable old woman who lived at Pontfaen in the Gwaun Valley. She was known personally to the Rev Meredith Morris who spent his childhood in the area around 1875. She had a reputation for visions and premonitions, and invariably she knew about deaths and funerals a fortnight before they happened. Her cottage was very close to the graveyard of Jabes Chapel, and she claimed that if she peeped out of her bedroom window at midnight, she would always see a "canwyll gorff" as a small quivering red light in the graveyard if a death was about to occur. She said that she could also see the light travelling about three yards above the road surface along the route that would be followed by the funeral procession. According to her, the light, having entered the graveyard, would stop for a minute or two above a certain place, and this is where the burial would eventually take place. Then, she said, the light would be snuffed out. She was in the habit of informing a few of her closest neighbours when she saw a corpse candle, and always she would be right about her predictions. Some considered her visions as miracles, but others claimed that she was a witch.

One day a sceptical man from outside the valley was visiting Pontfaen, and he heard about Hettie's special powers. He did not believe a word of what he was told, and issued a challenge to the old woman. He asked her to let him know when next she saw a corpse candle in Jabes graveyard, and to let him know the precise position at which the light stopped before it disappeared. Hettie was somewhat aggrieved at this lack of trust, but she agreed to the man's request.

After only a few days she sent a message to the sceptic. Apparently she had seen a light coming down the steep lane from Penrhiw and then past the Dyffryn Arms towards Jabes Chapel. However, she appeared somewhat puzzled and uncertain, as if doubting her own premonition, because the little light had stood over a spot in the graveyard where no burials had ever taken place before. This news was greeted with some hilarity by those who refused to believe in her special powers, for they also knew that all the burials took place at the other end of the graveyard.

Exactly a fortnight later a little child living at Penrhiw was taken ill with the croup and died. The funeral party came down the steep hill to Pontfaen and along the lane to the Chapel. When the party reached the graveyard they were asked by the minister to move to the far end of the hallowed ground. He had apparently decided that the normal place for burials now had inadequate space for further graves, and he thought it wise to begin to use another area. The grave that had been opened up by the grave-digger was at the exact spot where Hettie had seen the corpse candle glowing before it disappeared. After that, nobody ever disbelieved Hettie Howells again, and she continued to have her strange visions until the day that she died.

Strange Light at Cresswell Quay

It was a cold winter's night in 1850, and young George Griffiths was out for a walk beneath the sparkling frosty heavens. He lived at Cresswell Quay, which at that time was a bustling trading centre, with small vessels coming and going on the tide and carrying cargoes of coal, limestone and agricultural products. The lime kiln near the quay was burning brightly, and George decided that he would go and sit on top of the kiln for a little while in order to keep warm. As he sat there he looked down towards the blacksmith`s shop, and was surprised to see a light moving towards him. At first he assumed that he was looking at a man carrying a lantern, but as it approached he realized that he could see no trace of either a man or a lantern. It became apparent that he was looking at a pale red ball of light which was moving along about eight or nine feet above the road surface. George became very frightened and he felt his hair standing on end. As he watched, the light went slowly up the hill towards Pisgah Chapel. Then it disappeared. Afterwards George told several people about his strange experience. About a fortnight later old Betty Prickett died. Her funeral procession went along precisely the same route as the little light which George had seen. lt went up the hill towards Pisgah, where the body was buried in the chapel graveyard.

Betsy Morgan and the Lights

Betsy Morgan of Cresselly died in the year 1892, but for the ten years or so before her death she frequently saw corpse candles moving towards a field not far from her house. The candles would stop in the field, hover for a moment and then disappear. Her family and friends who knew about such things were surprised, since corpse candles were usually taken as signs of funeral processions to come, and they were supposed to disappear in graveyards at the position selected for the burial.

About a year after Betsy died Mr H Seymour Allen of Cresselly donated a parcel of land to the Primitive Methodists of the village, and on this land they built a new chapel with a commodious surrounding graveyard. By the time the Reverend Meredith Morris had come to the village in 1895 there had already been several burials in the new graveyard. The routes followed by the funeral processions were exactly those seen by Betsy in her visions, and the graves which were opened for the burials were in exactly the places where Betsy had seen the corpse candles disappear. In her lifetime she could not possibly have known that a future graveyard would be located in the field, for it was not even spoken about as a possibility before Mr Seymour Allen made his sudden and generous gift.

In South Pembrokeshire, once upon a time, once the sun was down, the darkness was very dark indeed......

The Lights of Doom at Tenby

In the old days there were so many tales of corpse candles, phantom funerals and other strange signs and omens that almost everybody in the country districts expected to encounter such things at some stage in their lives. One winter's evening around the year 1830, two ladies belonging to the family of Mr Richard Mason were returning home to

51

Tenby from a visit to Narberth market. They were much delayed on their journey, and it was well after midnight when they reached home in their hired carriage. The other members of the family, who had been rather anxious because of their late arrival, rushed to the door to receive them, and others went to the windows with their candles when they heard the sound of the horses' hooves and carriage wheels on the gravel of the driveway. By the light of several lanterns the ladies were helped down from the carriage, and after unloading their shopping the coachman set off towards his coach-house and stables, passing the churchyard on the way before disappearing behind the high hedge.

The next morning Mr Mason's gardener George was approached by an old man from the nearby village, who gravely informed him that a death was imminent in the family. "Now where didst tha get that idea from?" asked the gardener. "Not a shadow of doubt about it," replied the old man, sidling up to him and whispering into his ear. "I seen the lights!"

The gardener inquired as to what lights these might have been.

The old man glanced over his shoulder, as if afraid that he was being watched by the evil eye. Then he continued, speaking in a low hoarse voice. "The lights was here last night, sure as eggs is eggs," he said. "In the early mornin' hour it was, when all good folks is fast asleep. The corpse candles was at the doors and windows of the big house, and -- Heaven help the poor soul soon to be called to the Lord's bosom -- I even seen the phantom hearse lit up with ghostly lights. It come down the drive to the front door. There was big phantom horses pullin' it. An' I seen for meself that they galloped off up the drive to the churchyard, an' then disappeared! Then I looked back at the big house, an' the corpse candles had all gone. Nothin' left but the black black night an' the winter wind moanin' in the trees. Oh, terrible, terrible it was! When I watched me knees was quakin' an' I come out in a cold sweat. Even now, when I thinks of it, the hairs is standin' up on the back o' me neck." And with a final furtive glance over his shoulder, the old man concluded "You mark my words, George, death will strike this household afore the week is done. The lights is never wrong!"

The prophet of doom was greatly disappointed when George told him about the circumstances surrounding the very late return of the two ladies from their shopping expedition to Narberth.

In concluding this chapter, it should be noted that in the folk tradition of Pembrokeshire phantom funerals and fearsome and doom-laden sounds often go together, as do corpse candles and falling lights ("tanwedd" in Welsh). There is only one story in the whole lexicon of local ghostly tales involving a light at the head of a phantom funeral. Maybe there is something in the laws of physics which explains this apparent anomaly.

Chapter Five: Fearsome Omens

In this chapter we examine some of the strange supernatural tales told in Pembrokeshire over the centuries which relate to sombre events which have yet to happen. In the lexicon of the supernatural, we are dealing with signs, omens and portents, dreams, visions and nightmares, prognostications and predictions, prophecies, second sight and divination.

Phantom voices and even phantom birdsong occur in the stories, and a Welsh word which occurs over and again is "tolaeth", meaning a death omen in the form of a knocking or hammering sound or the sound of a tolling bell. Sometimes actual phantoms are seen (for example, the phantom steam train in Treffgarne Gorge or the phantom tomb seen by Mr John Pavin Phillips) but most often things are heard rather than seen.

There are links here with corpse candles and phantom funerals, and also with the activities of soothsayers, diviners and wizards. And again we encounter difficulties with scientific explanation. While ghosts may be relatively easy to explain as due to a "residual life force" left behind after a death, fearsome omens of things that have not yet happened cause us all sorts of problems. What are we to make of space and time if tomorrow has already happened as far as some people are concerned .... ? The stories that follow are. like those of the previous two chapters, very strange and very disconcerting.

The crags of Maiden Castle above Treffgarne Gorge, scene of the strange "phantom steam train" of 1770.

The Vision at Treffgarne

In the late eighteenth century a farmer's wife named Sarah Evans was renowned as a "dewin" (soothsayer) who had the ability to foresee future events. She was in all other respects a perfectly normal farmer's wife, one of the Bevan family of Market Mill who lived with her husband at Penyfeidr not far from Treffgarne Rocks.

From the slopes above the farm there was a fine view down into the spectacular and thickly-wooded Treffgarne Gorge, at one time renowned as a haunt of highwaymen and thieves and still regarded, in the eighteenth century, as a place very difficult of access. One day, around the year 1770, Sarah came into the house and described to her husband a most remarkable sight which she had seen in the gorge. Apparently she had watched a large number of heavily laden wagons or carts going very fast, one after another in a straight line, but with no oxen or horses pulling them. As if this was not strange enough, the first of the wagons had smoke coming out of it, as if it was on fire. She could not explain the vision, and neither could her husband.

Sarah Evans had her vision some 30 years before Trevithick first introduced steam locomotive power. But the vision became well known locally, and the story was passed down from generation to generation. At last it started to be looked on as a prophecy. When the railway came to Pembrokeshire in the 1850s the residents of the Treffgarne area thought that the prophecy was about to be fulfilled. But Isambard Kingdom Brunel and the other railway engineers were defeated in their attempts to extend the South Wales Railway northwards from Haverfordwest to Fishguard by lack of cash and by the steep gradients and extremely hard rocks in the gorge. Not until the turn of the century did the GWR manage to complete a railway line through Treffgarne Gorge.

On 30th August 1906 a line of carriages with a steaming locomotive in front thundered through the gorge for the first time, precisely as Sarah Evans had foreseen 136 years earlier. Soon there was a regular passenger service, summer and winter. And although diesel engines have now replaced steam locomotives, the carriages have continued to travel very fast through the gorge to this day.

Omen at the Rising Sun Inn

On a blazing June day in 1922 Mr William Ladd of Dolrannog Uchaf Farm, near Newport, set off in his pony and trap to do some shopping in town. It was haymaking time, and provisions were needed in order to feed and water the neighbours who would shortly be helping with the hay crop. As the pony approached the Rising Sun Inn it suddenly stopped and refused to go one step further. Mr Ladd was furious. He cursed and shouted, cajoled and pleaded, used the whip and used gentle persuasion, but still the horse refused to budge. William was forced to climb down out of the trap and take the horse by its halter, and finally the animal consented to be led past the spot. Then the farmer climbed back onto the trap and proceeded as normal down the hill into Newport.

Having done his shopping, William returned up the hill late in the afternoon, and as the horse drew parallel with the Rising Sun Inn, exactly the same thing happened. This time it was even more difficult to get the horse to pass, and it took a great deal of effort to drag the poor protesting animal to the safety of the roadway beyond. When he reached home safely Mr Ladd recounted this strange episode to his wife, and they both agreed that they had never before encountered such behaviour from a well-trained horse.

Next day, when all the haymakers were at Dolrannog, hard at work under the midday sun, one of them noticed that one man was missing. He lived in the little cottage next to the Rising Sun Inn. Somebody went off to investigate, and on reaching the cottage he hammered on the door, but got no reply. He had to force his way in, and was horrified to discover that the man had committed suicide during the night.

Premonition at Pisgah, Cresselly

Early one morning, while it was still dark, Mr John Thomas of Pisgah, Cresselly, heard a very strange omen. He was woken by a cry which seemed to be very close, and the voice was immediately recognizable as that of his sister. The voice came, so far as he could make out, from near the front door of his cottage. "Mother! Mother!" said the voice, over and over again. John got up out of bed and opened the door but there was no sign of anyone. So he went to the back door and opened that, and could still see no sign of anyone. His old mother who was in the house was woken up with all the commotion, and both of them were very mystified because John's sister was away on holiday at the time.

A few weeks later the sister was back at home, and John had almost forgotten about the strange incident. But then she was taken seriously ill, and within a few hours she had become delirious. In her delirium she shouted out "Mother! Mother!" over and over again, in exactly the voice which John had heard some weeks before. John was quite convinced that the phantom voice was a warning or "foretoken" of a forthcoming dangerous illness. Happily his sister did not die, but made a full recovery.

Night of Terror in Bridell

According to some old records, a very strange funeral custom was practised in parts of Pembrokeshire in past centuries. It was called "hirwen-gwd" (literally "long white bag" or shroud), and it was connected with the "gwylnos" or Wake Night. It was apparently quite common is some remote areas (such as the

Gwaun Valley, Pencaer and the Bridell-Cilgerran area) as recently as 1750, although it was greatly frowned upon by the church and by the civil authorities.

Following the death of a person, the corpse would be laid out in its coffin in the front room of the dwelling house, and would be watched over by friends and relatives throughout the Wake Night before the funeral.

Sometimes prayers would be said throughout the night on behalf of the dear departed. Often there would be a lighted candle at the head and the foot of the coffin, and young men would take it in turn (two or three at a time) to sit in the room watching over the corpse while the rest of the party chatted and partook of refreshments in the kitchen. As the centuries passed, what may have been originally a pagan ceremony (designed to prevent evil spirits from stealing the soul of the deceased) turned into a Christian ceremony and eventually into a macabre social occasion. In the early 1700s church elders were sometimes greatly disturbed by the horseplay which went on and by the amount of beer consumed during the long hours of darkness by the coffin watchers, although the Welsh Wake Nights seldom became as exuberant as those in Ireland.

The "hirwen-gwd" originated in a primitive belief that the soul of the deceased person must be given some help in leaving the body, and indeed in leaving the house where the death occurred. In most parts of Wales windows and doors would be left open during the Wake Night so that the soul could escape. But in Pembrokeshire there was an elaborate ceremony which involved the removal of the corpse from the coffin in its white shroud. First the fire in the hearth would be extinguished. Then some of the young men present would go outside, and with the aid of a ladder climb up via the roof of the house to the top of the chimney. There they would throw a rope down into the fireplace, and this rope would then be attached to the upper part of the corpse's body. Then they would haul on the rope, pulling the corpse right up the "simnai fawr" to the chimney top. There, it was supposed, the soul could escape to heaven, thus eliminating any chance of the house becoming haunted by an unhappy ghost in the future. This having been achieved, the corpse would be let down again and replaced gently in the coffin.

This ceremony was abruptly abandoned around the year 1760 following a strange and terrible happening at a Wake Night at a house called Pantycnwch, in the parish of Bridell. The story was told to Rev. Ceredig Davies by a Mrs Mary Thomas of Bengal, near Fishguard, and she had heard it from her old mother. On the fateful night most of the family of the deceased had gathered in the kitchen. Next door a jolly group of young men, having had too much to drink, were going through the motions of the "hirwen-gwd". But in addition to the custom of pulling the corpse up the chimney, it had become the custom in parts of Pembrokeshire for one of the group (presumably he who was most drunk or he who was bravest) to lie in the coffin while the corpse was absent. This was said to be necessary in

56

order to prevent the devil from taking over the empty coffin. Accordingly, after the removal of the corpse, one young man lay down in the coffin and made himself comfortable while the lid was replaced loosely. Amid great jollification the corpse was hauled up the chimney and let down again, and after untying the ropes the rest of the party carried the corpse back to the coffin. They took off the lid in order to let their friend out, and were horrified to find that he was dead ....

News of this terrifying event spread like wildfire throughout the community. Some said that the young man had suffocated; others said he had drunk too much alcohol; and some said that he had died from shock, having encountered the devil in the coffin. But whatever the truth of the matter, Pembrokeshire people were given a severe fright, and the custom of the "hirwen-gwd" was never again allowed as part of the Wake Night ceremonial.

Birdsong in Nevern Church

One of the great literary figures of Nevern was the Rev John Jones, who was also known by his bardic name of Tegid. Following a distinguished Oxford career Rev Jones was given the living of Nevern in 1842, and in the eleven years until his death in 1852 he was very active in the eisteddfod movement and in promoting Welsh culture generally. But he was also a good and conscientious minister, greatly loved and respected by his congregation.

The church and churchyard at Nevern saw several strange events surrounding the life and death of the bard Tegid.

57

According to legend, Tegid died on a Sunday morning. As he lay on his death-bed, a colleague from an adjoining parish was taking his service for him in Nevern Church. Half-way through the bible reading his voice was suddenly drowned by the most beautiful song of a thrush. The whole church was filled with the birdsong, and the congregation listened spellbound to its soaring notes. The minister stopped his reading and listened too. There was no bird in the church, and yet the sound echoed everywhere, along the nave, to the roof timbers, and around the altar. At last the birdsong faded away, and the church service continued.

After the service was over, the congregation heard the news that Tegid had died in the vicarage on the other side of the stream, just a stone's throw from the church. It was discovered that the song of the thrush in the church had occurred at exactly the moment of his death. A few days later, at the vicar's funeral, a thrush was again heard singing sweetly at the moment of burial. And stranger still, when the monumental mason came about twenty years later to install a tombstone commissioned by Tegid's admirers, he found a dead thrush on top of the grave.

Strange Prophesy at St Katherine's Church, Milford

Around the year 1770 a lead tablet was found in a well at Pill Priory near Milford. It had a Latin inscription on it, which was translated as follows: "When the highest part of the East is elevated in the House of God a great town shall be built, to which, with every wind and every tide, merchants from every clime shall come like bees to the flowers." The message was not well understood at the time, but in the 1780s and 1790s, as the new town of Milford began to take shape, local people began to look on the strange old message as a sort of prophecy.

In 1798 it so happened that the French warship L'Orient (The East) was sunk by Lord Nelson in the Battle of the Nile. One of the interesting relics brought home from the battle was the truck (masthead fitting) of the ill-fated warship. The truck was given by Nelson to his mistress Emma, Lady Hamilton; and she in turn gave it to St Katherine's Church, possibly on the occasion of the laying of the foundation stone in the year 1802.

When the church was completed in 1808 it was planned that the truck should be placed adjacent to a porphyry urn of Egyptian origin, which was to be used as the baptismal font. Charles Greville, who was the builder of Milford town, planned to place a suitably patriotic commemorative tablet, extolling the virtues of Lord Nelson, beneath the urn. But the whole plan was vetoed by the Bishop, who would not accept the use of a pagan urn as a baptismal font, and who found the glorification of Nelson's involvement in blood and carnage extremely distasteful. He suggested that the truck and the urn should instead be placed in the entrance to the chapel, and Greville had to agree.

58

We do not know whether Greville was aware of the old prophecy found in the well. But the truck was prominently displayed in the church until the 1830's, when it mysteriously disappeared. Some believe it was sent to the Royal United Services Institute in Whitehall, but it is more likely that it remained in the church, in a dusty and neglected state, among a pile of timbers in the church belfry. Later, when St Katherine's was renovated in time for its centenary, it was restored to its place of honour as the first object seen on entering the church. And then, in the 1920's, the truck really was removed to London, to be replaced by a copy made by a local craftsman.

All in all, neither the church congregation nor the townspeople of Milford have shown a great deal of respect for the truck; and therein, according to some, lies the explanation for the great hardship suffered by the town for most of its life. Maybe the strange prophecy of prosperity based upon thriving trade never will be fulfilled until the real truck is back in its rightful place, duly respected and properly cared for .....

The Phantom Tomb in Milford

In the year 1848 Mr John Pavin Phillips returned home to Milford Haven after a long absence. A few days after his arrival, he took a walk in the graveyard of St Katherine's Church, partly to enjoy the peace and quiet and the magnificent view over the Haven, and partly to see if any of his old friends and acquaintances had passed away during his absence and had been buried there. His eye was attracted by a fine new altar-tomb enclosed within an iron railing. He went up and read the inscription on the tomb, which informed him that a certain retired Colonel was buried there. He recalled that during his absence he had read of the sudden death of this gentleman, who had been the Assistant Poor Law Commissioner for South Wales. Apparently he had been seized with apoplexy while visiting the local Workhouse, and had died within a few hours. Mr Phillips had not known the Commissioner personally.

On returning home after his walk, Mr Phillips was asked by his old father where he had been. He replied that he had been up to the churchyard, where he had seen the tomb of the Commissioner who had died while visiting the Workhouse. "That is quite impossible," replied the old man. "There is no tomb erected over the Commissioner's grave." Mr Phillips objected, saying "My dear father, are you trying to persuade me that I cannot read? I was not aware that the colonel had been buried in the churchyard until today, and l only discovered that fact when l read the inscription on the tomb." After further argument Mr Phillips decided to go back and have another look. So after supper he walked up to the churchyard again. This time he failed to find any trace of the mysterious tomb. He knocked on the door of an old lady who lived near the churchyard gate, and asked her to show him where the Commissioner had been buried. She accompanied him back into the churchyard, and showed him an unmarked green mound in precisely the place where he had earlier seen the phantom tomb. Quite mystified, Mr Phillips returned to his home.

Two years later, the surviving relatives of the Colonel erected an altar-tomb, with a railing around it, over the grave. On hearing of this, Mr Phillips went along to have a look. The hairs rose on the back of his neck when he discovered that it was identical in every detail to the tomb which he had seen during his original visit to the site.

The Death Omen in Solva

In the Welsh-speaking areas of the county the "tolaeth" is a death omen, heard in the sound of a tolling bell or (more commonly) in the sound of coffin-making. Many people have heard the omen before a death, and carpenters have heard in precise detail the sounds of coffin manufacture in their workshops when they have been elsewhere.

One story of the "tolaeth" comes from Solva, where a fisherman and his wife were disturbed as they lay in bed on successive nights by eerie sounds downstairs. They heard shuffling feet, doors opening and shutting, chairs moving and men grunting as heavy burdens were set down on the floor. They were very frightened, since they knew exactly what the sounds meant.

The inner part of Solva Harbour, where the "tolaeth" was heard in a fisherman's cottage.

60

A few weeks later their son was drowned at sea. The first they knew of it was when his body was brought home on a ladder. With horror they realised that the sounds associated with the event were exactly those they had heard at dead of night --- the shuffling feet as the bearers entered the house with the corpse, the opening and shutting of doors, the moving of chairs to make room for the ladder, and the sounds of exertion as the men placed the makeshift bier on the floor.

The Kensington Hall Dream

One night in January 1910, Rev J. Ceredig Davies dreamt that he was walking near Kensington Hall, the country seat of Lord and Lady Kensington near St Bride's. In the dream he met Lord Kensington, who said to him "Go into the house. Lady Kensington is at home, and I'll join you in a few minutes." Rev Davies went to the front door, rang the bell, and was shown inside by the butler. He was asked to wait in the drawing room. There he waited for some considerable time, and was beginning to feel concerned when all the household servants came into the room, dressed in their holiday attire. They all looked concerned, and explained that Lady Kensington was not at home at all, but had got lost somewhere. They said that the Baron was hunting for her high and low, and was desperately worried because she seemed to have disappeared.

Rev Davies woke up feeling quite convinced that the dream had been a sort of omen, and that something had happened to Lady Kensington, who was a close family friend. A few days later the reverend gentleman read in his daily paper that the Dowager Lady Kensington had died in Calcutta in India. He discovered that her death had occurred on the very day of his dream, and that at the time of her death Lord Kensington was at sea, en route for India, frantic with worry, having been warned by cable-gram that she was seriously ill.

The Mark of Cain at Herbrandston

The village of Herbranston, not far from Milford Haven, has the unusual distinction that in two World Wars all of the local men who saw active service returned safely --- 24 in the First World War and 43 in the Second. It is said that a guardian angel has watched over the parish for centuries, and there is a tomb in St Mary's Church of a Crusader who miraculously survived the Holy Wars.

But one soldier who died violently is buried in the churchyard. In 1875 Lieutenant Phillip Walker of the Royal Artillery was stationed in nearby South Hook Fort. On 28th May, after a battalion dinner, there was a great deal of drinking and revelry. A bitter quarrel developed between Lieutenant Walker and a fellow officer, and as they struggled in a drunken rage the young man was stabbed to death. The murder trial caused quite a stir in the county, and the local people were outraged when the accused officer was acquitted. Phillip Walker, aged only 26, was buried behind the church of St Mary the Virgin, and his ivy-covered marble tombstone can still be seen.

South Hook Fort was the scene of a fatal drunken brawl between two army officers in 1875. According to legend, a consequence was "the mark on Cain" on the headstone of the dead man's grave..
(These, by the way, are chimney pots.)

Several months after the burial a strange manifestation was observed in the churchyard. Somebody noticed that following the installation of the headstone, a clear outline of a hand and a dagger had appeared. Many attempts were made to wash it away, but it remained indelible. Geologists may explain the mark as a result of selective weathering of the marble, but the old people of the village will still tell you that it is a sign of divine retribution --- the mark of Cain.

Disaster at Landshipping

In the year 1844 the Garden Pit colliery at Landshipping was the largest colliery in Pembrokeshire, employing 163 people. Many of the workforce, as was usual at that time on the Pembrokeshire Coalfield, were women, and there were also many boys under 14 years of age working at the coalface and hauling trucks on the underground tramways. The pit was located very close to Landshipping Quay. The main shaft was 65 yards deep, and the workings ran far out under the tidal estuary of the Daugleddau. Conditions in the pit were primitive and the owner, Hugh Owen, and his colliery managers were renowned as hard taskmasters.

On 13th February 1844 the workers at the coalface were seriously worried -- and not just because it was the thirteenth day of the month. The workings were shallow, and had been extended very close to the river bed, and that evening the men noticed with alarm that they could hear the sound of oars above them as the lighter vessels were rowed downstream on the high tide. A collier who was dumb noticed water leaking into the workings beneath the river and gesticulated to the foreman that the mine was in a dangerous condition. No action was taken, so he tried to pass on his message by scratching with a stone on the timber pit-props. The men expressed their concern to the manager, since they knew that tomorrow there would be a Spring tide which would bring a huge weight of water to bear over the Colliery workings. The boss would have none of it, and forced the next shift to go underground as usual.

Next day, St Valentine's Day, as the high tide surged up the river towards Picton Point, the roof of the workings collapsed and the Garden Pit was flooded by a catastrophic rush of water. The men and boys working underground had no hope of escape. Forty of them were killed, and there are still people living locally who believe that the real figure was seventy to eighty, with the official figure falsified because many of those lost were children supposedly too young to be at work in the pit.

After the disaster a mysterious notice, written in Latin, appeared on the headgear of the Garden Pit. It had to be examined by the vicar, who was the only person locally who understood Latin, and he translated it to the effect that the coal industry at Landshipping would never prosper again. The management swiftly removed the notice, but the next night it appeared again. The miners believed that a curse had been placed upon the Landshipping coal industry; and sure enough, no subsequent attempts at coal mining proved to be successful in the district either under the Owen family or their successors.

Invisible Hand at Cresswell Quay

George Griffiths of Cresswell Quay lived with his old mother in a house which also doubled up as his cobbler's shop. He used a room downstairs to practice his trade, and he used the same room as his bedroom. At one end of the room was his workbench, and at the other his bed with a small round bedside table beside it. In the year 1853 he was working late, finishing off a pair of boots at his work-bench. Suddenly he noticed that his bedside table was moving about, as if being dragged or pushed by a hidden hand. He jumped up, amazed and not a little frightened, for he could see no explanation for the table's movement. As he watched, the table was dragged across the room, its legs scraping along the floor, and then it came to a stop near the window. George moved the table back to the bedside, but he was greatly bewildered by what had happened, and could not get it out of his mind.

A few weeks later his mother's old aunt named Phebe Phillips came to live in the house. After only a few days she fell ill and died. Her body was carried downstairs into the cobbler's shop, and the bedside table, which was normally located between the bed and the wall, was dragged out and put near the window. Then some planks were placed on it and the body was properly laid out. Suddenly George's hair stood on end as he realized that the movement of the table, and the sounds it had made on the floor, were exactly those which had frightened him a few weeks earlier.

The Haunted Bell of Treindeg

This tragic tale was told to Francis Jones in the 1920s by a very old resident of Llandeloy, near Solva. In the old man's cottage Mr Jones noticed a battered sheep-bell hanging on the wall, and was told that it used to be haunted.

According to the old man, young Mr James of Lochmeyler met Miss Griffiths of Treindeg at Tancredston Fair. They were immediately attracted to one another, and began courting. Often Mr James would ride over to Treindeg to see his beloved. During the lambing season in 1644 Miss Griffiths was looking after some molly lambs. One of them became particularly attached to her, and on one visit Mr James promised that next time he rode over from Lochmeyler he would bring with him a little sheep bell that could be tied round the lamb's neck with a red ribbon. The young lady was enchanted, and said that the bell would be more than a means of knowing the whereabouts of her pet lamb - it would be a symbol of their love, and would remind her of her beloved every time it rang.

Before young Mr James' next visit there was turmoil in the area. Cromwell's troops had taken Roch Castle from the Royalists and in order to quell any future uprising many of them were billeted in local farmhouses.

There were frequent patrols on the roads and trackways. It was dangerous to travel at night, and the Roundheads said they would shoot anybody who was about after dark. However, love knows no restraint and young Mr James became desperate to see his beloved Miss Griffiths again.

So, one evening, he set off for Treindeg -- on foot, since this would attract less attention. After a long and muddy journey cross-country he could see the lights of Treindeg ahead of him -- but as he approached in the darkness he fell into a ditch and got very wet. The little bell which he held in his hand rang gently, disturbing the silence of the night. Unconcerned, he pressed on, but he was challenged by some dark shadows on the nearby road. Foolishly, he did not stop and answer, but ran on towards the lights of the house where Miss Griffiths would be waiting for him. As he did so the bell in his hand rang again. A volley of shots rang out, and the young man fell and died face-down in the mud.

The commotion attracted the people of Treindeg, and they all came out with lanterns. They found a group of Parliamentary soldiers standing over the body of the dead man. Miss Griffiths came too, and in the dim light of the lanterns she was composed enough to kiss the forehead of her dead lover and to take the sheep-bell from his hand. Mr James was buried a few days later, and within a few months Miss Griffiths was dead also, the victim of a broken heart.

Some years later the old house of Treindeg was burned down in a terrible fire, and among the ashes afterwards a workman picked up the burnt and battered sheep bell. He took it away and it remained in his family for many generations. All the family knew that the spirit of young Mr James resided in the bell, for occasionally it would ring of its own accord.

The old man who related this tale to Francis Jones heard it only once, when it rang gently at midnight (on the anniversary of the young man's death) for a minute or so. After that the old man took out the tongue of the bell, and he felt that it -- and the restless spirit of the young lover -- had been at rest ever since.

The Man Clad in Oilskins

JW Phillips's mother once related to him a strange story of an old friend of hers. It happened around the year 1850. She and her friend were staying in a large old house in the Pembrokeshire countryside together with various other young ladies. It was All Hallow's Eve, and the talk turned excitedly to ghosts, and witches, and strange phenomena. The bravest of the young ladies suddenly decided that she would try out a well-known superstition. The others tried to discourage her, but she persisted. She retired to her room and placed an article of her clothing on a chair in front of the fire. Then she settled down to watch.

Around midnight, when the house was very quiet, the girl became aware of a large man clad in oilskins, dripping wet, coming into the house. He looked at her intently. She was very frightened, for he had a fierce and forbidding expression. Then he turned on his heels and hurried out, slamming the door behind him. The hostess, and the other young girls, had been at the top of the stairs, but they neither saw nor heard anything except for a loud crash when the phantom visitor went out through the front door into the night. The girl fled from the downstairs room in a terrified state, and begged the others never to try that particular experiment for themselves. She took a long time to recover.

Some months later the same young lady was in the capital city, going over London Bridge. She looked across the street and saw the same man, dressed in the same wet oilskins. It was as if he had come up from one of the ships at the riverside. This time he was clearly no phantom; but made of flesh and blood. He was staring at her. She dared not return his gaze, feeling very alarmed and confused. Without looking back, she rushed on to her destination, her thoughts in a whirl. But later she met the same man at a dance. He had a surly expression on his face, and she thought him very ugly. She tried to avoid him, but he came up to her and asked her to dance, and although she wanted to refuse he held a sort of fatal attraction for her and she heard herself saying yes. They danced several times on that first evening, and went out frequently after that. Eventually they got married, although the girl's friends were all convinced that it was anything but a love match.

The poor girl was fated to be unhappy, for her new husband turned out to be a cruel and ill-tempered man. Her married life was one of constant pain and distress - a fact which she always blamed on the fateful experiment many years before on All Hallows Eve.

Presentiment in Tenby

JW Phillips was staying in Tenby for a weekend with an elderly gentleman who was a family friend. Several others had been invited for a house party, and together the guests, under the benign eye of their host, spent a pleasant two days of conversation and entertainment. On the morning of his departure, JW Phillips was sitting in the old man's garden when he sensed somebody coming up behind him and saying "The next time you come here will be the old man's funeral." He turned quickly, and there was no-one there.

Soon afterwards Mr Phillips said farewell and left for home in Haverfordwest. He was haunted by the strange premonition, and could not get it out of his mind. Later the same afternoon the old man went out for a drive in his carriage. Suddenly the horse bolted. He was thrown out of the carriage and was seriously injured. He died from his injuries the following Thursday. In the event Mr Phillips could not attend the funeral because of another previous engagement, but for the rest of his life the incident in the garden remained fixed in his memory.

There are many other stories in Pembrokeshire concerning prophecies and second sight, divinations and charms. We do not have space to relate these tales in this book, and in any case many of them are apparently quite mundane and unrelated to the spirit world. Other tales fall into the spheres of magic, witchcraft, folk beliefs and folk medicine. Some were included in the book entitled *Pembrokeshire Wizards and Witches*, published in 2001.

Chapter Six: Horrible Beasts

There are a number of interesting stories about phantom beasts in Pembrokeshire. Generally these beasts are considered to be inhabitants of the spirit world, and they appear in the course of hauntings, sometimes in the company of ghostly human beings but more often alone. Wizards or magicians are sometimes able to summon up these beastly spirits when they need help in some particularly difficult detective case. Generally they are extremely frightening to those who observe them. Sometimes they are recognizable as birds, cats or dogs, but sometimes they appear quite unlike any creature known to zoologists. Some of those which have an "almost human" appearance could be classified as goblins.

By the way, it should be mentioned that dragons do not count as Horrible Beasts since they are (or were) noble and real. Neither should we include the water horse, the water monster or "afanc", the mermaid or the giant in this chapter, since these creatures really belong in the fantastic and mysterious world of the Fairies.

The Little Corpse Bird at Eglwyswrw

In many parts of Wales there was a belief in times past in the "aderyn y gorff" or corpse bird, which would flap its wings against the window of a room as a portent of death. Sometimes it was believed that the death would occur in the room which had the affected window, but some people believed that the corpse bird could beat against any window in the doomed house. Maybe there is a deep psychological fear at work here, for even today most people dread the sight or the sound of a bird beating its wings against a window pane. This fear was no doubt reinforced by Alfred Hitchcock's famous film ....

Contrary to what one might expect, the "aderyn y gorff" is not a large black bird such as a crow or raven, but a small bird that would normally be thought of as harmless. Around 1870 Wirt Sikes found that the little bird would chirp at the door of the person who was about to die. But according to an old woman called Miss Griffiths who lived at Henllan, near Eglwyswrw, the corpse bird was very small and grey in colour. In the middle part of the last century she had four visits from this little bird. On each occasion it flapped at her bedroom window, first to warn of the death of her father, and then as an omen of the deaths of each of her three uncles in turn. We do not know whether the old lady had a fifth visit from the bird before her own death early in the last century.

The Hauntings at Freystrop and Merlin's Bridge

On Sunday 19 October 1890 Mr JW Phillips, a solicitor of Haverfordwest, was walking home following a visit to friends at Little Milford. Soon he was approaching the outskirts of the village of Merlin's Bridge. He was passing an old-fashioned house called Woodbine, at about 10.20 pm, when he saw a strange animal gliding across the road just in front of him. It was about the size of a fox, but whitish in colour. He was certain it wasn't a fox; the strange animal made no noise at all, but simply glided across the road, apparently oblivious to his presence. It then disappeared.

Some days later, on a cloudy moonlit night, Mr Phillips was passing the same spot, when he saw a very large black dog. At least, he thought at first that it must be a dog. It was as big as a St Bernard's, and was standing with its front feet on a pile of stones. On closer examination the creature proved not to be a dog at all, for it had the head of a goat, with horns. While Mr Phillips watched, it moved to the entrance of the lane and then leaped over a pile of timber into a patch of brambles, but in spite of its large bulk there was no noise at all.

Later, on November 10th, Mr Phillips was again walking home from Little Milford alone, around 10 pm. He heard an intense noise as soon as he left his friend's house. It sounded like the flapping wings of a very large bird, sometimes in front, sometimes behind, sometimes above and very close to his head. The noise continued all the way past Lower Freystrop, and followed him as he walked down into a hollow called Culvert Bridge.

There he met two strange and ghostly men who passed him without a word. Neither were they speaking to each other. Strangely, the noise of the "wings" stopped as soon as the men passed.

Mr Phillips continued towards the GWR Bridge near Merlin's Bridge. There he heard the flapping noise again. It got louder and louder and sounded like a panting noise followed by a deep-throated roar. At this point he became quite alarmed. He stopped and stood in a defensive posture with his stick raised, waiting for an attack from some animal.

Then he heard an almighty crash in the bushes on top of the fence and saw a huge black creature in the darkness leaping down into the road. It then rushed off up the hill towards Woodbine.

Mr Phillips walked many more times between Haverfordwest and Little Milford by the same route, but never again experienced these strange ghostly phenomena. But in 1920 he recorded that five other people had seen a large black creature ("between a dog and a calf") on the Pembroke Ferry Road about 2 miles from Haverfordwest. Merlin's Bridge people said that there was "fear" on that part of the road, and would not pass it alone during the hours of darkness.

Little Milford, on the estuary of the Western Cleddau -- the scene of several very spooky tales.........

The Strange Phantoms of Cresselly

Tom Phillips was a young man who lived at Cresswell Quay. In December 1842 he was courting a girl who lived near Loveston, and a friend of his was courting a girl from Thorn Farm, north of Cresselly village. After spending the evening with their respective sweethearts the two lads were due to meet up at 1 am at Thorn Lane Cross so as to walk home together. Tom arrived at the cross in good time and since there was no sign of his friend he settled into the hedge to wait, deciding that he might be somewhat delayed. He was not concerned, but after waiting for half an hour in the freezing cold he decided he could not wait any longer, and set out for home by himself.

He turned to set off along the Cresselly road, and was surprised to see a grey horse standing on the grass verge. He thought "What a spot of luck! I'll have a ride home to the Quay tonight." So he approached the horse, meaning to catch hold of its mane. The horse backed away. He made another approach, coaxing the horse gently, but again the animal backed away. So Tom made a rush at the horse, but this time it reared up and then took off, as if on hidden wings, and flew straight over a hedge nine feet high. Now that the horse had disappeared Tom began to feel frightened, for he could hardly believe his eyes. He walked quickly down the road, looking back frequently to see if the phantom horse was following him. It was not. Soon he was crossing Bishop's Bridge, but as soon as he reached the other side he heard a ringing and clanging of chains. He could see nothing, but the noise was terrific, and his hair stood on end. As he hurried on the noise travelled with him, and he soon reached old John Merriman's house. He thought of knocking on his door and asking for help; but since it was so late, and since he thought the old man would not believe his story, he decided to press on towards home.

Then the rattling chains stopped. Tom continued on his way, but after a few more yards he noticed on top of the hedge-bank a large earthenware pot with clusters of the most beautiful snowdrops he had ever seen. He was tempted to pick some of them, but they had a sort of ethereal quality, and he could not muster up the courage to try. Then the pot and the snowdrops disappeared. He continued to walk quickly and approached the main gate leading to Cresselly House. Opposite the entrance, right in the middle of the road, there was the most fearsome giant mastiff he had ever seen. He knew that there were no such dogs belonging to the big house, but there it was, menacing and vicious. Tom stood and the hound stood. Tom moved cautiously and the dog moved too. Tom sidled along the hedge, hoping to pass the dog, but it kept ahead of him, always the same distance away. Then, at the top of the hill, the dog disappeared into thin air. Tom reached The Shambles, shaking with fear, and sat in the hedge for quite a while as he composed himself and thought about which route to follow back to Cresswell Quay. Should he go through the village and knock up one of his friends? He thought he would only become a laughing-stock if he did, and so he decided to continue alone, taking the longer path via the Vicarage and The Grove rather than following the lane past the Norton, which was reputed to be haunted.

He passed the Vicarage and was opposite the entrance to The Grove, when he suddenly saw in front of him a man with no head, with a long pole over his shoulder. As he watched in horror the ghost walked ahead of him, crossed over a hedge, then walked across a field, and disappeared over a hedge at the far side. Again Tom was terrified, and he ran the rest of the way back to the Quay. When he reached the culvert, he felt that at last he was safe.

Next day Tom went to see his sister-in-law Patty Phillips, who lived at The Back. She was older and wiser than him, and when he told her of his adventure she seemed not at all surprised. "Let that be a lesson to you, Tom," she said. "You've bin troubled by hobgoblins right enough. They was sent as a warnin' to you against goin' out courtin' at such hours on a Sunday night. Such things can only lead to mischief."

After that, Tom never again went out courting on a Sunday evening, and never again walked the same route between Thorn Farm and Cresswell Quay ......

70

The Hound of Baal down in the Cwm

Once upon a time there was a sea-faring man "of pronounced rollicking habits" who lodged with his brother in Cwm (Lower Town, Fishguard) when on land. One night the jolly sailor was returning happily from Cefn-y-dre to the Cwm, when on reaching the bridge over the Gwaun River he had an unpleasant encounter with the great black Dog of Baal.

The infernal dog was of huge size, sooty black, with flaming red eyes as big as oysters. He had a chain around his neck, which crashed and rattled as he bounded towards the sailor. The poor man was paralysed with fear, and became quite convinced that the creature was going to seize him and carry him off for his sins to the very hot regions far below, where Baal is said to dwell. As the dog rushed at him open-mouthed, with a muffled roar like the sound of distant breakers in a hurricane, the terrified sailor man cried out to God for mercy.

The Dog of Baal was about to sink his great fangs into the sailor's leg, but as soon as the name of God was uttered the creature sprang back, with a howl of rage that rang from the top of Pen Twr on the one side to Carn Mawr on the other side of the valley. Then, with a parting glare of fiendish fury, it leaped into the river and disappeared.

The intended victim, when he saw that the Cwm end of the bridge was now clear of the enemy, rushed to the front door of his brother's house and kicked and beat upon it in a panic. Then, when his brother opened it, he fell in a faint upon the threshold. The sailor's brother and sister were much affected by this incident. As for the sailor himself, it is said that he actually went to church on the Sunday following his encounter with the infernal hound -- something which was very much out of character.

Phantom Hound on Cot Moor

During the nineteenth century a certain Mr David Walter was walking across a field called Cot Moor, in which there are two standing stones called the Devil's Nags. These stones were said to be haunted, but Mr Walter did not believe such things, being a deeply religious man. Suddenly, without any visible sign of beast or man, he felt himself being lifted up in the air, upon which he was unceremoniously dumped on the other side of a hedge.

Next time he went for a walk across the field he took a strong fighting dog mastiff with him for protection, but as he approached the Devil's Nags, he saw blocking his path the apparition of a dog more terrible than any he had ever seen. In vain he tried to set his mastiff onto the beast, but his dog crouched by his master's feet and refused to move. Mr Walter then picked up a heavy stone, thinking that this might frighten the hound. Immediately a circle of fire surrounded the animal, and in the bright light he could see the fearsome fangs and grinning teeth, and caught a glimpse of a white tip to the long tail. The dog then disappeared -- but Mr Walter knew that he had seen one of the infernal dogs of hell.

The Phantom Ape at Carew Castle

One of the most famous ghostly stories in Pembrokeshire concerns the Carew Ape, which is Castle supposed to have lived in the castle in the early part of the seventeenth century. The animal's master was the extremely wicked Lord of Carew, one Sir Roland Rhys. According to legend, Sir Roland's son seduced the beautiful daughter of a local Flemish tradesman named Horwitz, and when the outraged father came to the castle to complain the arrogant Lord set his tame ape (probably a chimpanzee) onto him. The poor man was almost killed by the brute, but at last Sir Roland called it off and his horrified servants were able to take Horwitz away and tend his bleeding wounds.

The tradesman was so seriously injured that he could not travel home, so he had to spend the night in the castle. As he lay on his bed he cursed Sir Roland under his breath and prayed to God that he would suffer as he himself had done.

Later that night Horwitz was half-asleep and trying to obtain some respite from the pain of his injuries when he was horrified to hear screams of terror echoing through the castle. On and on the screams went, some of them sounding human and others like nothing he had ever heard before. At last the screaming began to grow weaker; and then there were great gasps of agony, followed by a low wailing sound. After what seemed to be an eternity in Hell, the sounds died away altogether. Horwitz was so petrified by this experience that he hardly dared move, but then he smelt smoke and realized that the castle was on fire. Painfully he dragged himself downstairs to the Great Hall, and there an appalling sight met his eyes. Sir Roland lay dead on the floor in a pool of blood, horribly mutilated by his pet ape. In the struggle some burning logs had been dislodged from the fire, and now the ape, too, lay dead in the midst of a blazing inferno.

The terrified tenant staggered from the castle, leaving Sir Roland's servants to fight the blaze, but a sizeable part of the castle was damaged in the fire. Horwitz never returned to the castle after that, but even now, after four hundred years, the locals say that the shadowy figures of Sir Roland and his ape can still be seen haunting the ruins. And those who have ears to hear can still hear the spine-tingling screams of man and beast in their last and fatal encounter.

Chapter Seven: Strange Hauntings

Sometimes particular places or individuals may be troubled or haunted by supernatural activity even where no actual ghosts may be seen. Almost certainly ghosts are involved, but for some reason they may not manifest themselves. Instead, they may be content with throwing pots and pans about, knocking ornaments off walls or mantelpieces, overturning heavy pieces of furniture, switching electric lights off and on, hammering on doors and windows, and making unpleasant sounds. In other words, there is a definite interaction between the spirit world and the physical one which ordinary mortals find very unnerving.

Poltergeist activity is extremely unpleasant and destructive, because it appears to involve a malevolent intent on the part of some troubled spirit. It has often been noted that it occurs when adolescent males or females are in the vicinity, and in some stories a young man or woman appears to attract or even cause poltergeist activity. Perhaps a sort of sexual energy is involved in the process, just as a medium provides the energy for an unseen spirit to manifest itself as a ghost.

In this chapter we also examine hauntings involving baleful disembodied voices, inexplicable forces or barriers which affect some people but not others, phantom armies, flashbacks or nightmares, persecution of an individual who has done something dishonest, the "gwrach y rhibyn", and phantom visitations involving funereal sounds. There is even a strange story about a flying farmer ....

The Poltergeist at Orielton

Some of the earliest folk tales of Pembrokeshire are to be found in the writings of Giraldus Cambrensis, an inveterate twelfth-century recorder of tit-bits of information. This tale -- one of the earliest poltergeist tales on record -- is about the grand house of Orielton, now a Field Studies Centre but then much smaller and simpler in appearance.

In 1190 Orielton belonged to one Stephen Wiriet. It appears that a curse had been placed upon the house, for the poor man and his family and friends were greatly troubled by an "unclean spirit". In Welsh, such a spirit would have been called a "bwgan". The spirit threw dirt at people, "more with a view of mockery than of injury", but also conversed quite freely with visitors. Apparently it also had strange powers, for it could look into past history in a way that was somewhat embarrassing.

According to Giraldus, in reply to the taunts and curses of visitors, the spirit "upbraided them openly with everything that they had done from their birth, and which they were not willing should be heard or known by others". Stephen Wiriet sought to exorcise the spirit from the house by invoking the help of various clerics, but the place could not be purified that easily, for the spirit appeared unaffected by the sprinkling of holy water or by religious ceremony. Even worse, the priests themselves, although supposedly protected by the crucifix and although greatly respected as devout men of God, were "equally subject to the same insults".

Giraldus related that the bewitching of the house was so severe that poor Stephen Wiriet was eventually reduced from affluence "to poverty and distress" as the Orielton estate fell upon hard times.

The Haunting at Castlebythe Farm

The remote hamlet of Castlebythe is located in the western foothills of Mynydd Presely, to the south of the lonely valley of Cwm Gwaun. It is an area of bleak open moorland, seldom visited by strangers and renowned for its ghostly happenings. This story is a classic one, involving a poltergeist and a teenage girl.

One evening around the year 1900, the family of Castlebythe Farm were seated around the fire in the flickering light of paraffin lamps when the silence was broken by a voice. It seemed to come from outside, but on investigation nobody could be found, and as the voice continued a chill of fear descended on the family. After a while silence returned, soon to be shattered by a clattering noise outside. Someone investigated, to discover that the big butter churn in the dairy was turning end-over-end with nobody near enough to turn the handle. There was a large stone rattling inside it, and it was only with the greatest difficulty that the men of the family managed to stop the churn to get it out.

Next night the whole episode was repeated, and so it continued night after night. Word of the haunting spread around the area, and some neighbours came to hear the strange voice and see the tuming butter churn for themselves. The spirit or "bwci" appeared harmless, but it was a nuisance nonetheless. At last, with the family greatly irritated by the supernatural activities, some of the men decided to keep watch with a shotgun for protection. They hid behind some big trees, and heard the voice but saw no movement. The next night they kept watch again. They thought they saw something move near the dairy, so they let fly with both barrels of the shotgun. There was a flare of light in the trees, but that was all. As the men trooped back inside, the farmer suddenly noticed that the one person apparently unaffected by all the commotion was Marie, the servant girl, who was sitting quietly in the corner as usual. He sensed that there must be some link between the girl and the eerie visitations, and next day he dismissed her from his service. After that, the strange voice was never heard again, and the butter churn remained quiet in the dairy.

74

The Persecution of John Mathias

A Pembrokeshire man called John Mathias once caused himself great trouble following the death of his wife Martha. He knew that she had not completed a proper will, so while her corpse was still warm he placed a pen in her hand and then directed it with his own hand so that it wrote out a brief will leaving all her worldly possessions to him. At the foot of the page he wrote "signed by my own hand, Martha Mathias." Afterwards he swore on oath that he had seen his wife write out the will, and so he inherited all her savings and her property.

Later John Mathias married again, and immediately he was afflicted with signs and hauntings. Strange noises occurred in the house, crockery was flung about and broken, doors were locked and unlocked by unseen hands, candles were extinguished and Mr Mathias and his new wife became very scared. They sold the house and moved to another - but still the hauntings continued. Even in chapel, where he was a deacon, the poor man would sometimes rise to his feet in the middle of a sermon and would appear to be struggling with some unseen adversary. Naturally, this caused great consternation among his fellow worshippers. So troubled was he that the air seemed to chill when he approached, and his children became very disturbed.

At last the foolish man recognized the reason for the haunting; he gave away all his wife's money and possessions to other relatives, and from that day on he was troubled no more.

Hiraeth at Bettws Ifan

In the parish of Bettws Ifan, not far from Cenarth, there used to be a house called Penrallt Fach. Around the year 1883 it was occupied by a tailor called Samuel Thomas and his wife. One morning, very early, Samuel was woken up by a heavy knocking at the bedroom door. He asked "Who's there?" but received no reply, and everything went quiet again. The next morning, again very early, he heard a heavy knocking at the front door. It was so persistent that at last he got out of bed, calling out "All right, I'm coming. I'm getting out of bed now." He went downstairs, opened the door, and was surprised to discover that there was not a soul to be seen anywhere. He was perplexed about this, and made a note in his diary as to the date. After this, he was not troubled by the phantom knocking for some time.

Then, a year to the day later, in the first week of January 1883, Samuel's brother came to visit him. The two men went out shooting during the day, and in the evening Samuel went into his tailors workshop to do some work on a suit. Suddenly he heard two sharp knocks on the window. He went to the window and looked outside, but there was nobody to be seen. Then the knocking resumed, and went on for about ten minutes. On the second night the knocking started at about ten o'clock and continued until eight o'clock the next morning. On the third night the knocking resumed on the same window, and Samuel and his brother decided to try and discover what was going on. But every time they looked at the window or went outside to investigate, the knocking stopped, and every time they turned their attention to other matters, it resumed again. Several other young men from the neighbourhood came to investigate. They all heard the knocking, and all were equally mystified.

Now the word had got around the community that there was a "spirit knocking" at Penrallt Fach. On the fourth night some of the older neighbours came along, including the farmer who was Samuel's landlord.

They all heard the knocking, and all became convinced that there was something supernatural about it. On the fifth night a very loud knock was heard on the front door of the house, as if somebody had charged at the door and was trying to break it down. On the sixth evening Samuel went out for a walk and was scared out of his wits by a tremendous noise which he described as the sound of "two hundred horses rushing towards him". By now Samuel and his wife were getting thoroughly frightened. On the seventh night there was more knocking, and when the knocking continued on the eighth night the tailor went out with his gun to threaten whoever or whatever was causing the disturbance. However, outside he heard a dreadful groaning voice in the air, and then a doleful wailing sound the like of which he had never heard before. Certain that he was hearing the terrible "gwrach y rhybyn", he ran inside and locked the door.

After this, there was no more knocking or wailing, and life at Penrallt Fach returned to normal. However, some years later a Mr Lloyd from Newcastle Emlyn called at the house. He related that at the precise time of the "spirit knockings" he had been in America, at the bedside of an old woman who had once lived at Penrallt Fach. Her husband had died in the house, and she had emigrated to America with her family shortly afterwards. She was close to death, and when she realized that she could not return home to Bettws Ifan to die she was inconsolable, crying and moaning in her delirium as she slipped away over the course of a week or more. Mr Lloyd had been at her bedside when she died, after a final and heart-rending cry of "hiraeth" or longing after her old family home in Wales. This final act in the old lady's struggle against death coincided exactly in time with the wailing and groaning which concluded the strange events experienced by Samuel Thomas at Penrallt Fach.

Tragedy at Pontfaen

Some years ago a Welsh historian was researching the family history of the Gwaun Valley, and during her studies she came across some references to a terrible event which had occurred near Pontfaen during the wars between the Normans and the Welsh princes. During a skirmish, a troop of enemy soldiers descended on the community and killed all the menfolk. Then, totally out of control, they ravished the women one by one and then drowned them in a pool of the river Gwaun.

One day, the historian was relating this tragic story to a local farmer who lived near Pontfaen. As she talked, a look of amazement came over his face. "This is indeed very strange," he said. "Only a fortnight ago a young lady knocked on my door and asked if she could walk down to the river across my field. She was from Llandysul, and as far as I know she had never been to this area before. She explained to me that she had been having nightmares, night after night, and that her dream was always the same. Apparently, in the dream, she was tortured and raped by a group of men, with her agony ending only as she slid into the water. Then, as the water closed over her, she found peace. And always, on waking, she knew that she had to travel to a certain place in the Gwaun Valley which she could see in her mind's eye. Not knowing the Gwaun valley, she resisted for a long time, but at last, as the dream was repeated over and again, she could resist no longer. So she drove over one day, travelling slowly along the valley road until she recognized the place. That was when she knocked on my door and asked to walk down to the river."

Apparently, having found the spot where the terrible deed had been done many centuries before, the girl exorcised the dream and travelled back to Llandysul, having found peace.

Dark Presence at Cwmslade

When Dick Harries was 14 years old he left school and went to work at Morfil, a big farm not far from Castlebythe. At that time the farm was owned by a Mr Harries, no relation to Dick, who had moved into the area from England. Early one morning, when Dick turned up for work, Mr Harries said to him "Good moming, Dick. Those wretched cattle have got out again. They are up in Cwmslade. I want you to go and fetch them back." "Yes yes," replied Dick. "I'll go and fetch them now." "Well," said the farmer. "There is no great hurry. You had better have your breakfast first and fetch them after."

So Dick had his breakfast and then set off for Cwmslade. He could see the cattle near the old cottage in the cwm ahead of him. Before he reached the animals he came to the little stream which he had crossed many times before via a couple of convenient stepping stones. As he tried to jump onto the stones he suddenly became tight-chested and started gasping for breath. He tried again, but felt that something was smothering him.

Every time he tried he lost his breath, and at last he thought to himself "I can't manage this. I'd better go back to the farm and tell the boss that there is something strange at the stream, so that I'm unable to fetch the wretched cattle."

Dick turned to go back to the farm, but then felt rather foolish. Convinced that Mr Harries would not believe him, he returned to the stream and tried again to cross it. Again he was seized with panic, and struggled for breath. Furious that he could not cross such a tiny stream, with the cattle so close, he at last gave in and went back to the farm.

When he explained to the farmer what had happened, Mr Harries said "Oh, don't be silly." "I'm sorry, but I just can't get over the stream!" said Dick. "What's wrong then?" "When I try to jump onto the stones I lose my breath." "But that's ridiculous!" "I just can't do it." "Oh, very well then. I'll come with you."

And so they both walked up to the stream where the cattle were. Watched by Mr Harries, the boy tried to jump across, but again became quite breathless. He stood rooted to the spot, gasping for air. So the farmer jumped across, without any trouble at all. Turning to Dick, he said "What's wrong with you? Come on -- jump!" The lad tried again, but again he lost his breath. Quite unable to understand what was affecting young Dick, Mr Harries collected the cattle and got them back across the stream. Then together the two of them drove the animals to the farm.

For years afterwards Dick tried to find some explanation for what had happened that morning in Cwmslade -- but he could only conclude that there was some dark presence there which refused to allow him to approach the cottage.

The Haunting at Molleston

In the year 1833 Jane Fortune lived with her parents at a cottage called The Pools at Molleston, near Narberth. An old couple called Ben and Betty Davies lived next door. Mr Fortune worked at Pembroke Dockyard during the week and only came home at weekends. Normally he arrived home on a Saturday and returned to his lodgings in Pembroke Dock late on a Sunday evening.

One Monday morning in the middle of winter old Betty died in her sleep. She was buried on Wednesday. In the middle of the night after the funeral Jane heard a great commotion next door. She and the family wondered what could be the matter with old Ben. Early next morning he came into the Fortune's cottage and said that he had slept hardly at all because "something was dumbering" all night long. On Thursday night the noise was repeated, this time very loudly. Neither Ben nor the Fortune family slept a wink, for all of them were terrified by the noise. Next day Ben confided to Mrs Fortune that he was worried about Betty's spirit coming back to haunt him. On Friday night the noise was unbearable, and it was accompanied by the heart-rending cries of someone in great distress. Ben was so frightened that he called at the Fortune's house at dawn and said he could stand it no longer. He would have to leave his cottage. Later that afternoon Mr Fortune came back from the Dockyard, and he was sad to hear of the death of his neighbour while he had been away.

He was also told about the strange events which had occurred following the funeral. For a long time he thought in silence, and then he said that he would stay in Ben's house for the night to see if he could discover the cause of the problem. Ben was very grateful for this offer, and he was given a bed in the Fortune's house for the night. At bedtime Mr Fortune went next door to spend the night, with everybody listening intently. Sure enough, round about midnight the noises came, but they did not last for very long and after half an hour they faded away. Then Mr Fortune returned to his own house. He looked pale, and to Iane and the rest of the family he appeared numb and frightened by some experience which he would not talk about. In his hand he carried eight pence and a halfpenny in coppers. He handed the coins to his wife and told her that they had come from a hidden drawer in an old chest in the bedroom, and that they were to be handed to the Tea-man when he called on Monday morning. He said that Betty owed the money to the Tea-man from last week's visit.

When the Tea-man called at Molleston on Monday Mrs Fortune asked him if Betty owed him any money. "Oh yes," replied the Tea-man, "She owes me eight pence halfpenny from last week for a little bag of tea."

Mrs Fortune paid over the coppers and the Tea-man went on his way. After that there was no more haunting of the house, for Betty's spirit was at peace after the payment of her debt. Jane and the rest of the family knew that Mr Fortune must have encountered her ghost and received instructions from it, for he could not possibly have known about the debt or about the hiding place that old Betty used for keeping her household coppers.

The Old Man taken by the Devil

On the south-facing slope of Carningli, not far from Newport, there is a farm called Dolrannog lsaf. Here, towards the end of the eighteenth century, an eerie event occurred which has become a part of local folk-lore.

A wicked old farmer, who had made no secret of his dislike for all matters religious, had died and was laid out in his coffin. The "Gwylnos"or wake night went on as normal, with many people calling to pay their last respects and with much merriment among family and friends. Candles were lit in the room where the body lay in its open coffin. As peace descended on the house in the early hours a few of the male members of the family maintained their vigil in the room next door.

Suddenly the relatives were startled to hear the sound of horses' hooves approaching at a gallop. They heard the horses stop outside the front door, but before they could investigate the house was plunged into darkness as all the candles were simultaneously extinguished. They heard

79

the sound of heavy footsteps outside; then the front door was opened and the footsteps came into the house. They were all frozen with fear. Nobody spoke and nobody moved. But they all felt and heard the invisible intruders go past them into the room where the corpse lay in its open coffin.

Caersalem Chapel, Cilgwyn. A coffin full of stones is reputed to be buried in the graveyard.

Then the intruders went out again. The heavy footsteps reached the front door, which was then closed. All those present heard the sound of the horses being mounted again, and then off they went at a gallop into the distance. At last, all was silent again.

At first everybody was too frightened to investigate. But then somebody managed to relight the candles, and the feeling of terror began to subside. Cautiously, the men entered the room where the body had been laid, only to find that the coffin was empty. In spite of a frantic search the body was never found, and it was concluded by the family and neighbours that the Devil had come to claim his own. The coffin was filled with stones and later buried in Caersalem graveyard, with a minimum of religious ceremony, just for the sake of appearances.

David and the Charnel House at Pill

In the early 1800s there was a strange fellow called David who lived in the village of Pill (near Milford). He was assumed to be mad, for he was quite fearless, and took to sleeping every night in the charnel-house near the church, among the piles of human bones and skulls. One day the local lads determined to give David a fright, and a few of them dressed up in white sheets and crept up to the charnel-house at dead of night. They then proceeded to make eerie noises, moving back and forth in front of the charnel-house door and pretending to be ghosts.

However, they got more than they bargained for. Far from making his hair stand on end, the lads caused David to wake up in a furious temper. And knowing precisely what real ghosts were like, he chased off the intruders, shouting "O you are devils sure enough, and I am David of Pill, so here's what you get!" And with that he started throwing stones at the lads in white, causing them to suffer from an assortment of cuts and bruises.

David continued to sleep in the charnel-house for several weeks after this, but one night he encountered something more than a normal ghost, and fled in terror from his house of rest. After that, he returned home and refused ever to go out again after dark. His family and friends were firmly of the opinion that he had encountered an extremely unpleasant supernatural being in the dark shadows among the piles of white bones.

The Phantom Armies seen at Mynydd Morfil

Mynydd Morfil is one of the lower foothills of Presely, not far from Puncheston and Pontfaen. The area round about is one of bleak windswept moorlands, with few farms and no proper clusters of settlement. There are two stories from here about phantom battles in the sky. This is the older of the two. One night in 1853 Mr John Meyler of Cilciffeth was walking home from Morfil. As he passed Penterfin he was distracted by a vision of armies in the sky. There were two armies, clearly visible overhead, locked in a life-or-death struggle for supremacy. As he walked on he watched the spectral armies become larger and larger, till at last there were thousands of warriors, many on horseback, galloping at each other, with horses and men falling under the assault of enemy swords, spears and battle-axes. Mr Meyler was so terrified by the vision that he called at Penbanc, where Mr James Morris lived. Mr Morris came outside and together the two men watched the battle for a further two hours. Then the vision disappeared and Mr Meyler continued on his way.

It has been suggested that this vision was a premonition of the Crimean War which started about six months later. However, it is more likely that Mr Meyler and Mr Morris were watching a "ghostly replay" of the Battle of Mynydd Carn, a terrible encounter which took place around the year 1081 between the armies of Gruffydd ap Cynan and Rhys ap Tewdwr on the one side and Trahaearn and Caradog on the other. This battle was crucial in the struggle for supremacy between the Welsh princes round about the time of the Norman invasion. At Mynydd Carn there was appalling loss of life, and the battle is well recorded in the ancient annals of Welsh history.

But the site has never been found. One of the most educated guesses is that the battle took place in the wild hills around Morfil and Castlebythe.

Flying Farmer at Eglwyswrw

It was a fine calm moonlit night in winter, and David Thomas of Henllan was walking home along the main road from Eglwyswrw towards Felindre Farchog. He had been into the village to fetch some medicine for a sick animal from the shop. Suddenly, at about 7 pm (afterwards he remembered the time quite clearly), he found himself in total darkness, being carried through the air back to Eglwyswrw by a "crefishgyn" or spirit. When he felt his feet on the ground again he realised that he was back in the middle of the village, hanging onto the iron bars of the churchyard gate. During his flight he had passed the blacksmith's shop, where several men were at work; but they had not seen him, nor had he seen them, while being transported through the air.

This is a strange story of transport *towards* the churchyard, for there is a tradition that St Wrw, the local female saint who was buried in the chantry chapel, was so pure that she "would not have any bedfellows".

Consequently she would cast out any male corpse that happened to be interred there. In other words, any flying corpses encountered would be en route out of the churchyard rather than towards it .....

The Field of the Dead near Llanychaer

On the slopes above the Gwaun Valley, not far from Llanychaer, there is another white lady haunting at a place called Parc y Meirw (which means "The Field of the Dead"). It is a spooky place, and it is said that there was once a terrible, bloody battle here between the armies of two Welsh princes. Some people believe this to be the site of the Battle of Mynydd Carn, which took place in the year 1081.

This particular battle is more likely to have taken place on Mynydd Morfil, but whatever the truth of the matter it appears that the field was used as the burial place for hundreds of dead warriors and their horses.

Along the edge of the field there are the remains of the largest stone alignment in Wales. At one time there were eight tall stones embedded in the ground. The shortest was five feet in height, and the tallest twelve feet. According to legend, the stones were erected to commemorate the fallen soldiers. Now four of the stones have fallen over and the rest are embedded in a hedge bank.

Local people are still very reluctant to walk past Parc y Meirw after dark, and some prefer to make a long detour of a mile or more even during daylight hours. It is said that a white lady haunts the field on dark nights, always following a certain invisible trackway. White ladies tend to be relatively harmless. But there is also a darker legend associated with the site, and in the 1800's it was believed that there was a "prehistoric hobgoblin" at Parc y Meirw, which had the power to kill any person who trespassed onto the haunted ground after dark.

Chapter Eight: Terrible Goblins

There are not many stories in Pembrokeshire about goblins, and there is some doubt among the experts as to whether they belong to the realms of ghosts, fairies or demons. In the Welsh tradition the word "Bwca" or "Pwca" is used for a goblin or elf, but the Bwca is normally benign, and is attached to a particular house or cottage in order to perform some sort of service to the residents. He is comparatively harmless, but is more like a familiar spirit than a fairy, and in many stories he is associated with the signs and symbols of magic or witchcraft. Sometimes he leads people through much tribulation to a hidden treasure; in the next chapter the story from Southernpits, near Lawrenny, is a typical example.

The Bwcci or Bwcci Bal, on the other hand, is very definitely an evil spirit, and he comes in a number of guises. There is an extremely long tradition of goblins inhabiting the Gwaun Valley, and this is specifically mentioned in the "Life of St Brynach". The saint's biographer records that following various unfortunate experiences at Milford Haven, Brynach eventually found his way to north Pembrokeshire. There he lived an interesting life in which devils and angels figured prominently. He was very intent upon missionary work, and founded a number of churches in the Gwaun Valley, at Henry's Moat, and at Cwm-yr-Eglwys. His main church was at Pontfaen, but life was made very difficult for him there by the presence of assorted evil spirits (goblins and devils) which had made the area almost uninhabitable. Every night they wandered about, frightening the local people with their "dreadful outcries and horrid howlings". Through his persistent ministry Brynach at last managed to subdue these evil spirits, but he was not happy at Pontfaen and he was eventually told by God to move with his little band of disciples to the valley of the River Nevern. There he found things to be much more peaceful and comfortable.

Flying Goblins at Roch Church

An interesting feature of goblin stories is the ability of these unpleasant creatures to fly through the air with the greatest of ease. Flying goblins appear in one particularly interesting story about the parish churches at Llangwm and Roch, more than ten miles away.

Inside the Llangwm church there is an effigy of a crusader, clad in full armour and with a sword in his hand. The face is handsome and expressive, and the head rests upon a plumed helmet. The thong of the boot, twined around one leg, bears some resemblance to a serpent, and this gives a clue to the identity of the person portrayed in stone. According to tradition, the crusader was the first De la Roche (called by the locals "Dolly Rotch"), the builder of Roch Castle who died from the bite of a viper.

Adam De la Roche (if indeed it is he who lies entombed) was a feudal lord who controlled large tracts of country in the old hundred of Rhos. The family had extensive estates in the Llangwm and Benton area, and it was they who built the church. There is an old legend that when Adam died he was buried in Roch Churchyard, not far from the castle gate. Next morning, it was discovered that the grave was open and the coffin gone, and a message eventually arrived that it had been discovered in the porch of Llangwm Church. Servants were sent to bring the body back. This they did, and the coffin was re-interred at Roch. Next night the same thing happened, and the servants had to fetch the coffin back again. This happened on two more occasions, causing the servants and family to suspect that some supernatural forces were at work. So they determined to sit in the Churchyard and watch the grave throughout the night. As they sat there in the darkness, and as the midnight hour struck, they were amazed to see "a multitude of dwarfs and flying serpents" in the air. Transfixed with fear, they watched, helpless, as the phantom visitors dug down into the grave, lifted up the coffin, and flew off with it in the direction of Llangwm.

After this, it was agreed by all that the goblin spirits would not let the cowardly Adam rest at Roch, and so the coffin was buried in Llangwm Church, where it remained undisturbed. Greatly relieved, the family eventually erected a monument over the tomb, complete with symbols relating to his life and death.

The Evil Spirits at Bowett

In 1855 Jonathan Davies, who worked at Lamphey Court, went off to Bowett near Hundleton to see his girl-friend. He had heard that Bowett was haunted by all sorts of evil spirits, but he had never seen or heard anything of them himself. Later on, as he and his beloved were sitting in the kitchen, they heard an almighty crash out in the hall, and pots and pans started rattling everywhere. They went out to investigate, but there was nothing to be seen. They sat down again in the kitchen, intent upon continuing with. their courting, but no sooner had they done so than they heard an eerie groaning and moaning noise from the hall. They rushed out, but again they found nothing. After this experience the couple decided that the atmosphere was not quite right for courting, so Jonathan took his leave and the girl went off to bed. As the young man came round from the back door into the yard he saw quite distinctly three spirits flying away from the house. He watched them as they travelled through the air, and when they were some way off they suddenly disappeared in a cloud of smoke. Jonathan never again visited Bowett after dark, and he maintained to his dying day that the house was haunted. Indeed as late as 1900 the old people of the neighbourhood used to refer to "strange sounds and peculiar happenings" at Bowett.

The old farm at Bowett, near Hundleton, where Jonathan Davies saw three evil spirits in 1855.

The Naked Goblins on Presely

In the Presely Hills there are many stories of encounters with ancient, awful beings, and there are many who believe that elemental forces still reign supreme among the rolling bleak moorlands and jagged rocks. Not long ago a local man who had been a boxer in his younger days was walking alone near Foelfeddau, which is Welsh for "the bare hill with the graves". He was a big man, very fit and seemingly afraid of nothing in this world and probably little in the next. He was alone and utterly content, and had been walking for several hours in the quiet of the day, listening to skylarks above and other moorland birds around him.

Suddenly, as though a curtain had fallen, all about him changed completely and he felt the raw edge of fear. He felt that he was in the presence of the unknown. He looked about him. Everything looked the same, but now there were no sounds -- no birdsong, no rustling of the breeze in the grass, no bleating of sheep. This was the dreaded "Presely Silence", which others have felt in the past and others will feel in the future. He stood still, feeling danger in the air and waiting for something to happen.

He became aware that evil, invisible eyes were upon him. He swung round, but there was nothing there. A low laugh came from alongside him, as if he was being taunted by a "bwgan" or goblin. He turned again, but still could see nothing. He began to feel giddy and he sat down on the turf, closed his eyes and put his hands to his head. When he opened his eyes again he saw a group of small, hairy men, quite naked, carrying heavy clubs. They were walking towards him, muttering and laughing among themselves. They paid no attention to him, but came closer and closer and closer. He tried to get to his feet and found to his horror that he was held in a vice-like grip by some force he could not explain. He had always been a strong man but he found that he was quite powerless to move. With mounting horror he watched the approach of the small hairy men. Then he screamed with terror, closing his eyes as he did so.

When he opened his eyes again all was normal. The skylarks were singing, and he could hear the bleating of lambs in the distance. There was no sign of anyone - the goblins had disappeared without trace. Scrambling to his feet, our friend rushed away from the accursed spot. Afterwards, in relating the story, he said that he has tried to convince himself that it was all a bad dream. But he said that wild horses would never drag him to that place again.

The Bwcci Bal at Cilgerran

On 21st August 1850 a farmer was returning home from Ffair Laurens (St Lawrence Fair) in Cilgerran, having sold all his cattle and having enjoyed a jolly evening with his friends and neighbours. He had to walk alone along the road at Glanpwllafon, which was at that time overlooked by dark and gloomy woods populated by ancient oaks and soot-black shadows. Suddenly he heard rapid and heavy footsteps behind him, and assuming that somebody was wanting to pass him, he stepped aside. But nobody passed, and the footsteps fell silent. A little mystified and afraid, he continued on his way through the dark shadows, and heard heavy footsteps behind him again. He stopped, but again there was only silence and the faint sighing of the wind in the trees.

Now he was thoroughly alarmed, and walked as fast as he could. But as he walked faster, so did the heavy footsteps behind him. At last he dared to look over his shoulder, and he saw a huge shadowy form beneath the trees not far behind him. He broke into a run and sped towards the safety of a little cottage that he knew was not far ahead -- but even as he ran he could hear the steady thump of the gigantic feet hitting the dirty roadway behind him.

At last the farmer reached the safety of the cottage and banged on the door, but as soon as he arrived the Bwcci Bal disappeared. When he had recovered, the man showed the cottager the great splashes of mud on his back, which he swore had been thrown up from the muddy lane by the monster's feet.

Chapter Nine: Ghostly Treasure

The stories in this chapter are relatively straightforward, and all are based on the old belief that a person who goes to the grave carrying some dreadful secret about hidden treasure will return in ghostly form until invited to divulge the secret. He or she will haunt an individual or a house until a "medium" is found who can be entrusted with the secret.

Then, through a series of complicated adventures, the site of the treasure will be divulged, the medium will recover it, and the ghost will as a consequence be released from earthly ties. The ghost then goes off voluntarily to the spirit world and the haunting ceases, leaving the chosen individual to become wealthy and successful.

These "treasure stories" from Thorn Farm, Southernpits, Trewern and Stepaside have a certain charm about them. They are more complete and complex than many of the other stories in this book, and while they are still eerily recognizable as ghost stories there are no real villains in them, and while we read them we sense that we are sharing an experience of justice being done. In a book so full of shadows and horrors it is no bad thing to remind ourselves that ghosts and hauntings do not exist in order to inconvenience us; rather they exist because there are sad spirits who require release and who need our help in order to escape from earth.

Alternatively we should sometimes recognize that it is sometimes our misfortune to simply "get in the way" of something that is happening in the spirit world. There are undoubtedly evil spirits about, but we can take Rev Aelwyn Roberts' word for it that the great majority of spirits are harmless and are even inclined to help -- if they can -- those of us who still inhabit the land of the living.

The Seven Gold Coins

About three hundred years ago a teenage girl was engaged as a servant by a farmer's wife who lived on a small farm somewhere in Pembrokeshire. She seemed happy enough, but after some months it was obvious that something was worrying her, and at last she went to her mistress and asked for her release. On being asked the cause of her concern, she explained that whenever she went alone along a certain lane near the farm on overcast dark nights, she met a strange shadowy figure of a man. If she changed her route, the figure did the same. The man never appeared in bright moonlight. When this reached the farmer's ears, he advised the girl to confront the stranger if she was followed again, and to ask him what he wanted. Somewhat against her better judgment, the girl agreed. Next time she was followed she asked the shadowy figure why he kept on frightening her, upon which he beckoned for her to follow. This she did, and she was led to a small field not far from the farmhouse. The man seemed harmless but sad, and he asked her to come to the same place next night with a shovel. "But, my dear," he added, "You must not say a word of this to anybody."

The girl said nothing to the farmer and his wife, and next night went to the field with a shovel. The ghostly stranger was there, and he led her to a spot in the corner of the field. "Now you must dig," he said, "right here where I am pointing." The girl obeyed, and eventually discovered a pot full of gold coins. Then the shadowy figure told her that the coins were hers, but that she should always keep seven of them and hand them down to posterity. So long as she kept this trust, her family would enjoy good fortune and prosperity. At last, looking relieved that he had fulfilled his mission, the ghost took his leave and disappeared.

Shortly after this the farmer's wife died. After a period in mourning, he asked the servant girl to marry him, and she agreed. A year later they were man and wife. Then one dark night, the ghostly stranger appeared to the girl for the last time. He directed her always to be careful in handing the seven coins down, always from father to son, or from mother to daughter, from generation to generation. If this was done, he said, the farm would always remain in the family and would prosper. If, on the other hand, she or any of her descendants lost or spent any of the seven gold coins, or gave them away, the estate would lose property and land in proportion to the number of missing coins. She listened intently, and said that she understood. And so, with his work complete, the ghost gave a faint smile, and disappeared, never to be seen again.

The girl now shared her secret with her new husband, and they agreed to keep faith with the mysterious figure who had bestowed upon them this ghostly blessing. The coins were handed down, as instructed, from generation to generation, and none of them has been spent, or lost, or given away to this day. The farm has grown into a large and wealthy estate with hundreds of acres of land and many tenant farmers. Each new generation of the family has been told the story and each one has kept the family secret. As a result the estate is still intact, and the family is now the wealthiest in the whole of Pembrokeshire.

Ghostly Messenger at Narberth

A **gentleman** who lived in the neighbourhood of Narberth was greatly troubled by a ghost. He was so haunted and tormented that his life became a burden to him, and he did not know what to do. Every night he feared to go to bed, and when he did at last get off to sleep he would be woken by the ghost, which always called him by name.

He would have to leave his bedroom and try to get some sleep elsewhere, but even then the ghost pursued him. He could both hear the ghost and see its shadowy form. At last the squire decided that he would have to obtain some protection from the ghost, and he got two of his farm lads to sleep on either side of him. But at a certain time each night he would be woken by the ghost, although the farm lads remained fast asleep. And each night he would have to rise and leave his room, quaking with fear. When he could stand it no longer he asked a local Wise Man to call and see him. In a state of despair, with his head buried in his hands, he cursed his tormentor. But the Wise Man explained that the ghost was probably trying to lead him to some place which was causing it anguish. The Wise Man also said that ghosts must be confronted and interrogated, and he advised the squire to do just that.

So next night, when the ghost appeared, the frightened squire plucked up the courage to ask the ghost what it wanted. At once the ghost beckoned for him to follow. He got up from his bed, followed the ghost downstairs and outside into a neighbouring field. There something happened which has never been revealed. But the locals assumed that the squire must have been told to dig at a certain place, where he discovered a treasure of gold and silver. At any rate, having disposed of its secret, the ghost faded away, and never troubled the gentleman again.

The Ghost of John Paul Jones on Caldey

John Paul Jones was a Scot who became a famous pirate in the latter part of the Eighteenth Century. He was an excellent seaman with little respect for the law, and after throwing in his lot with the Americans he was a considerable thorn in the flesh to the Excise men of England and Wales. According to legend, whenever he was operating around the western coasts of Britain, he would come in to the island of Caldey for water and supplies; and indeed Paul Jones's Bay is named after him. During the 1700s there were many rumours that local people helped the pirate in his irregular activities, and a tradition has survived that when he died in 1792 he was buried on Caldey, with his body being pushed into a crevice in the rocks near Small Ord Point.

It is still claimed on the island that the ghosts of John Paul Jones and his fellow pirates can be heard and seen burying treasure on his favourite beach. Sometimes there are strange bumps in the night, and the sounds of large stones being moved about. One encounter with the ghostly pirate band occurred in the early 1920s when Miss Renee Haynes was undertaking "psychical research" on Caldey. It was a calm and quiet evening, and Miss Haynes was sitting on the terrace of the house called Ty Gwyn. She could see the last embers of the sunset in the West, and the twinkling lights of Tenby on the mainland. She could hear no sounds but the mild splash of the waves on the ebb tide. There were a few voices chatting inside the house. The monastery was dark and there were no lights on in the Caldey settlement, but it was already too dark to dig properly without a lantern.

Suddenly Miss Haynes heard, with great clarity, something which was quite unexpected, namely the sound of iron spades digging down through sand and pebbles and occasionally striking rock. The sound went on for some time, indicating that the diggers were involved in a substantial task. Miss Haynes was not at all frightened by the ghostly digging, and a few days had passed before she recalled the legend of John Paul Jones and the buried treasure.

Talking of Caldey Island, the phantom monk referred to in Chapter 2 was sometimes linked in the years between the two World Wars with a mysterious "Glastonbury Treasure", which is said to have been brought from Somerset in the time of Henry VIII. Apparently the monk who was entrusted with its safe-keeping became convinced that it was in danger from pirates, and so he concealed the treasure in a secret chamber and bricked it up from the inside, thus condemning himself to death in the process. A "luminous glow" is supposed to mark the site of the treasure.

The Ghostly Visitor at Stepaside

In 1820 a certain Joshua Davies of Stepaside was greatly troubled by ghosts. As soon as he retired to bed he would be tormented by them, and he found it impossible to sleep. At last he went to consult a local witch, and she told him that when next he was visited by a ghost he must get up and get dressed. Then, she said, the spirit would go outside, and he should follow. This he did.

As predicted the nocturnal ghost went outside, crossed over to a hedge at the far end of the garden and motioned to Joshua to dig at a certain spot. He fetched a mattock from the shed and did as he was instructed. At length he came upon an earthenware pot. He opened it up and found inside a magnificent silver inkstand. He carried the treasure towards the house with him, and the ghost, which had been looking on, promptly disappeared.

But before he could reach his back door two hobgoblins appeared out of nowhere and chased after him, and he was struck several times by sharp stones which they threw at him. He fled indoors and shut the door with great relief. The hobgoblins did not trouble him any further, and after this uncomfortable episode he kept the inkstand in the house, suspecting that he would be very unwise ever to dispose of it. He was never again troubled by ghosts and hobgoblins, and slept happily ever after.

Down by the river. Tangled branches, dark shadows, strange noises in the night.........

The Goblin at Southernpits Cottage

This story comes from the Lawrenny district. Once upon a time there was an old cottage at Sudden Pits, not far from Coedcenlas on the road to Cresselly. Nowadays it is called Southernpits. The cottage has gone, but the farm remains. An old couple lived in the cottage in abject poverty. One winter's night, very late, the old man had gone to bed and his wife was tidying up in the kitchen and preparing to follow him. She heard a very strange noise outside in the yard, and for a moment she listened at the door, becoming convinced that something or someone was coming towards the house. She decided that it was probably a heifer which had broken out of the neighbouring field, and so she went outside to drive it away. She was greatly surprised to see a strange looking goblin in the back yard. He was only a few yards away from the door and he was preoccupied in drawing a circle in the mud with a heavy club. The wife got such a shock that she screamed and started to close the door, but the goblin fixed her with a penetrating gaze so that she was unable to move. He spoke not a word but indicated to her through signals that she should fetch her husband. This she did and after getting dressed the old man came downstairs.

The old couple stood at the back door and watched the goblin complete the drawing of the circle in the mud. Then he stopped work and beckoned to the couple to follow him. He stopped in the comer of the yard and indicated to the old man that he should fetch a mattock and start to dig.

Although he was very frightened by this strange experience the old man obeyed and dug a deep hole at the spot indicated. At last he came upon a large pottery jar and broke it with a single blow of the mattock. He was amazed and delighted when he saw that it contained hundreds of gold coins. The goblin smiled a strange goblin smile, showing his milk-white teeth, and a flame came out of his mouth. However, so preoccupied were the old couple with their wonderful discovery that they quite forgot to thank the goblin, and his pleasure turned to anger. He growled a frightful growl, and proceeded to beat the old couple with his club until they were black and blue. Then he lifted the club high above his head, and thunder and lightning came out of his mouth. Then, as they cowered in the corner of the yard, the old couple saw that on top of the hillock above the cottage there was a solid gold chariot drawn by two jet black boars and driven by two sleek greyhounds. The chariot came down the slope at breakneck speed, driven by the greyhounds as they cracked their whips. To the ears of the old couple the sound of the wheels was like the most terrible thunderstorm. The chariot came straight towards them, and they thought they would be run over, but it swerved, and as it passed they saw one of the greyhounds grab the goblin by the hair and drag him into the chariot. Then off they went into the distance like a hurricane, never to be seen again at Southernpits.

The old couple were almost scared out of their wits by this experience, but when all was quiet again they saw that the broken urn and the gold coins were still there in the hole. They gathered up the coins, filled in the hole, and thereafter continued for many years to enjoy their good fortune. Their rise from abject poverty to comfortable living was frequently commented upon by their neighbours, but they never revealed how they had come by their unexpected wealth.

The Golden Idol of Trewern

Trewern is an ancient house not far from Nevern and about a mile from Pentre Ifan. It was owned at one time by the wealthy Warren family. In the eighteenth century, and for as long as anybody could remember, the house had been haunted. Strange noises were often heard in the rooms, dishes would dance about in the kitchen of their own accord, and sometimes a lady dressed in a long silk dress would be seen. There appeared to be more than one ghost in the house, and although many attempts were made at exorcism the hauntings continued. The house was struck with misfortune, and in 1757 there was no male heir to the Trewern estate for the first time in 700 years. The last of the Warren family, old Edward Warren Jones, died a bachelor at Trewern in 1829, and the mansion fell into other hands.

Finally, things became so bad that nobody wanted to live at Trewern, and it seemed that the house would be left to its fate and would fall into ruin. But then, around the year 1840, the fortunes of the old house were transformed. The farm was let to one David George, a farmer and Baptist minister of Caersalem and Jabes. He had two old servants, surviving as best they could with few of the luxuries of life. But then Rev George suddenly acquired fine clothes and new furnishings. The old house was repaired and tidied up. New farm animals were purchased. And the servants were seen buying food, wine and other household items on a lavish scale. New farm buildings were built, and the land was improved through better husbandry.

All of this needed money, but try as they might the neighbours could not discover where it was coming from. For several years Trewern continued to rise in the estimation of the neighbours, but still none of them could work out the reason for Rev George's new-found wealth. The mystery deepened when it was noticed that he regularly left Trewern in his coach and stayed away for several weeks, and that whenever he returned there would be more lavish expenditure.

At last, in 1875, the farming minister died and the secret leaked out. It was revealed by an old servant that one of the resident ghosts of Trewern had told him of an "image of great value" sealed inside the wall of an upstairs room, immediately above the main entrance. A search was made, and sure enough a large pagan idol, made of solid gold, was found in a hidden recess. Rev George swore his servants to secrecy, and started to turn the image into money. Every now and then he would knock off a piece of the image, melt it down in the Dolbont smithy, and set off with the gold nuggets to London, where he would sell them at the best possible price before returning with hard cash. In this way, over the years, he sold the whole image, and nobody was the wiser. After the image was found and fully disposed of, the ghosts of Trewern disappeared, never to return.

The "Druid's Cave in Tycanol Woods

So the good times returned to the old house. David George remained a tenant at Trewern and continued in the ministry. He became a substantial figure in local affairs, for example representing the Baptists on

93

the Nevern School Board. But ready cash was clearly not a problem for him. He purchased four neighbouring farms and built two new ones. It was also rumoured among the neighbours that the pagan image had been stolen hundreds of years earlier from an ancient Druid site among the oak groves of Pentre lfan or Tycanol, which would account for the haunting of the old house. Interestingly enough, there is still a local belief in "Druid caves and groves" in the woodland.

The Terrible Exorcism at Thorn Farm

We end this book with one of the most complete and interesting ghost stories ever told in Pembrokeshire. It is frightening, amusing, and true to life, and it is also a story of virtue rewarded. The old farmhouse at Thorn, near Cresselly, was occupied by a widow and her family. They were very disturbed by unearthly sounds, which could be heard every night in the same upstairs room. The sounds could be heard proceeding along the landing towards the top of the staircase, where they would fade away. Nobody could be induced to sleep in the haunted room, and indeed as the nights passed the haunting became so noisy that nobody could get any sleep. At last the family was forced to leave the house each night and sleep in the barn across the yard.

The widow was desperate for help, so she called in to see the parish priest and explained everything to him. "Don't worry," he said. "I'll put everything all right." True to his word, he called at the farmhouse the same evening. He said he would stay in the farmhouse alone that night, in order to learn the nature and cause of the disturbance. So when everyone else had gone off to spend the night in the barn the parson was left alone. He prepared to settle down for the night, and armed with prayer-book, tallow candles and tinder-box he went upstairs and lay down, fully clothed, on one of the beds. He lit a candle and started to read aloud from his prayer-book. After about half an hour there was a loud crash downstairs, and he heard heavy, irregular, clumsy footsteps coming up the stairs. He kept on reading in a vain attempt to calm his nerves. Then he heard heavy breathing and he knew there was something in the room with him. He looked up and there stood a large lean horse! "In the name of the Lord," said the parson, in as loud a voice as he could manage, "What have I to do with thee? Away hence!" And with that the horse reared up, turned and vanished from sight.

The parson was greatly relieved, but before he had a chance to feel too self-satisfied there were more noises downstairs. More footsteps came up the stairs, this time brisker and lighter. The parson kept on reading out loud from the prayer-book. He heard a snort from the side of the bed, and on looking up he saw that a shaggy-haired bullock had entered the room.

He repeated the same words, and the bullock disappeared. An hour elapsed, and the priest thought that everything was finished. He began to

94

doze off, but sat bolt upright when there was an almighty crash downstairs, followed by the loudest and most fearsome noises he had ever heard. He thought that every room in the house must be filled with phantoms rushing about madly in terror. His hair stood on end as he wondered what might happen next.

Then he heard lighter, almost human, footsteps coming up the stairs. He kept on reading aloud from his prayer book. From the corner of his eye he saw the bedroom door open, and there stood a strange-looking little man, beautifully dressed in gold apparel, with rings on his fingers and jewellery around his neck. He made a polite bow to the priest, who said "Good evening, sir. Kindly take a seat." The little man sat on the corner of the bed. "In the name of the Lord, speak!" said the priest. And then the elegant phantom said "Why did they not ask me to speak before? I have come from the land of spirits, and I have paid these people many visits, but they have never had the courtesy to speak to me or ask me my business. Had they shown better manners, it would have been to their advantage, and I would have ceased to trouble them long since. Now I want you, sir, to carry out the few but important instructions that I am about to give you. If you don't, woe betide you. If you do, neither you nor they will ever see me again." The parson nodded and confirmed that he understood.

The little man continued. "The instructions are these. An ancestor of the widow and her family left behind him a pile of money, and laid it in an earthen pot under the staircase. It is buried a full yard beneath the far left corner of the biggest flagstone. This fact you must convey to the family in the morning. They are the descendants of the old miser who buried the treasure, and they are the rightful inheritors of his estate. You are to instruct the widow to dig for the treasure herself, and to divide the money between herself and her children -- half to her and half to them. And you, merciful priest, for your trouble, are to take the grains of corn that will be found at the bottom of the pot, under the coins. These are my instructions. See that they are carried out to the letter, or in future I will give you a great deal of trouble."

After this curious speech, the little man said "Now I am going to leave you. Which way would you prefer me to depart, in sound, in fire, or in both?" "As you like," replied the priest. "Very well then," said the spirit, "I'll go in sound." He gave a deep bow, turned and went out of the room.

The priest heard footsteps creaking down the stairs, and then he heard the front door bang as the spirit went outside. Then there was the most fearsome wailing, like all the demons in hell, followed by rolls of thunder, one after another, louder and louder until the noise was unbearable. The poor parson thought that his soul would be carried away on the waves of sound, and he cried out "Lord, have mercy on me!" And suddenly the noise stopped, and the priest realized that the only sound he could hear was the throbbing of his own heart. That was the end of the disturbance, but the priest could not sleep.

95

Thorn Farm near Cresselly, the scene of a famous and terrible exorcism in the eighteenth century.

Exhausted and haggard after his experience, he watched and waited for signs of light in the dawn sky, and as soon as the first sun's rays touched the house he heaved a sigh of relief. He got up and went down to the barn to wake up the family, who had slept right through all the commotion. He called them to the hearth in the kitchen and recounted the whole story, passing on the strange speech of the spirit as exactly as he could. Then the widow went and fetched a shovel, and dug beneath the stairs. A full yard down she found the crock of gold. She put half on one side for herself, and gave the other half to the children. At the bottom of the crock there were some handfuls of grain, and these were given to the priest. Not a single grain was left in the crock. He put the grain in his pockets, and with the heartfelt thanks of the family he set off for home tired but elated.

The family became immensely wealthy, and bought lands and animals, fine clothes and fine furniture for the house, much to the astonishment of the neighbours. The parson did not fare badly either, for when he arrived home he found that the grains of corn in his pocket had been transformed -- every one had been turned into a golden guinea.

✳✳✳✳✳✳✳✳✳✳✳✳